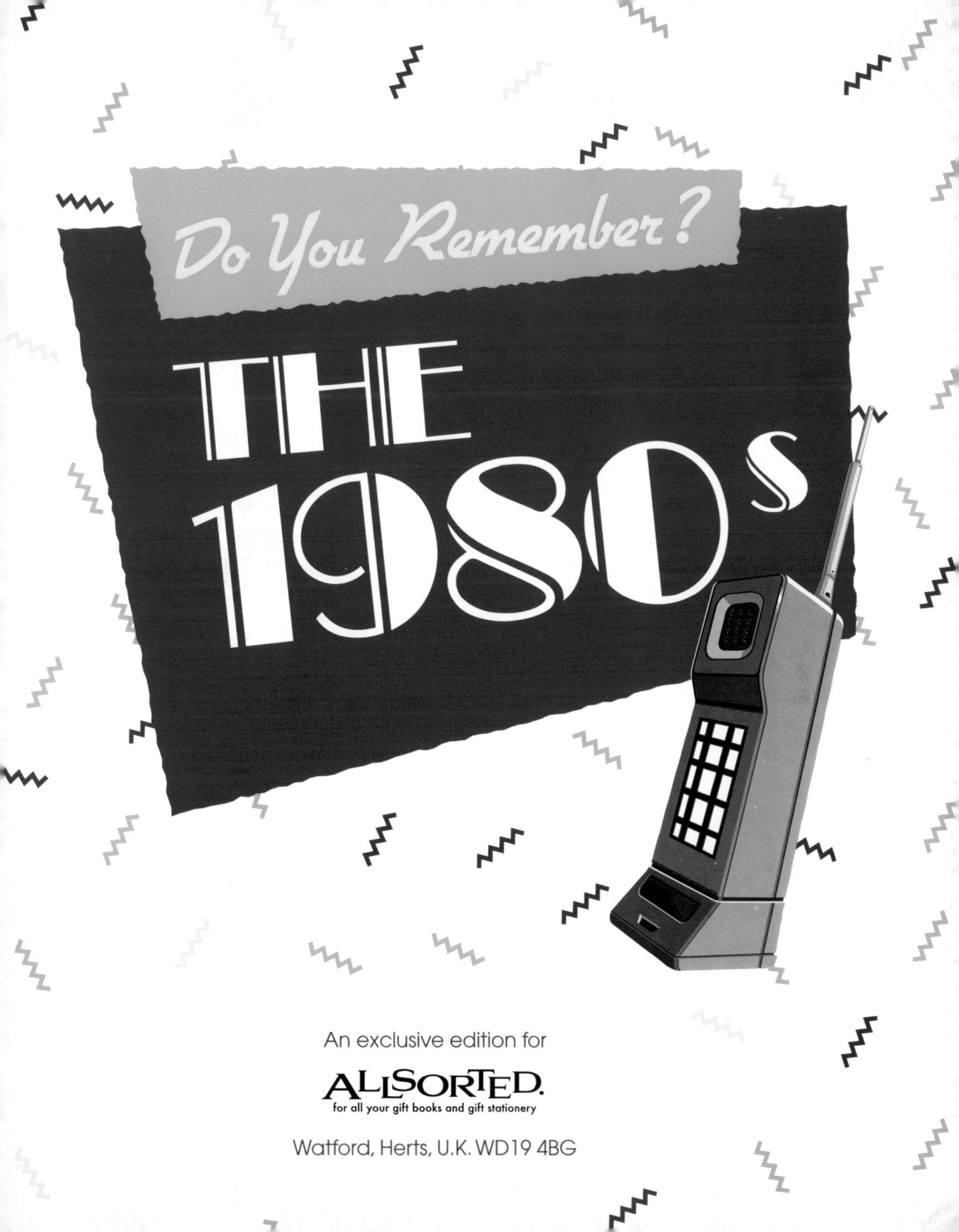

An exclusive edition for

ALLSORTED.
for all your gift books and gift stationery

Watford, Herts, U.K. WD19 4BG

Published in 2016 by Allsorted. Watford, Herts, U.K. WD19 4BG

Compiled by Michael Powell
Illustrations reproduced courtesy of Shutterstock.com
Page 6, Marina Bolsunova; page 21, 360b; page 60, Cath Vectorielle, page 88, Dario Vuksanovic; at Shutterstock.com.
Concept by Milestone Design
Designed by Joanna Ross at Double Fish Design Ltd

Printed in China

Every effort has been made to ensure the accuracy of the information contained in this book. In the unlikely case of queries please contact the compilers via their website www.susannageoghegan.com.

Introduction

The eighties were excellent. Well, you should know because you lived through them. This special decade witnessed the first computer virus, the last fight of Muhammad Ali and did you know that in 1983 a pint of beer cost just 76 pence?

You could hear Ultravox, Tina Turner and Rick Astley on the radio and watch Molly Ringwald, Eddie Murphy and Steve Guttenberg on the big screen. Torvill and Dean danced the Bolero, NASA launched its space shuttle fleet and everyone fell in love with Chicken Kiev. What a great time to be growing up.

Well, that was all a long time ago, but you'd be surprised how many memories you can refresh with a little encouragement. In this book you'll find 54 quizzes and more than 1,000 questions covering world events, music, films, celebrities, fads and crazes, fashions, comedians, actors, singers, inventions, advertisements, novels, toys, sporting greats, scientific achievements and lots of things that made your eighties childhood unique.

Some of the questions will be easy for you to answer but almost impossible for those without your personal experience. Other questions will call up random memories to make you smile. All those real moments have disappeared but you will always have this book to remind you!

Contents

The Year That Was – 1980 6
The Year That Was – 1981 8
The Year That Was – 1982 10
The Year That Was – 1983 12
The Year That Was – 1984 14
The Year That Was – 1985 16
The Year That Was – 1986 18
The Year That Was – 1987 20
The Year That Was – 1988 22
The Year That Was – 1989 24
Classic Eighties Novels 26
Diana, Princess of Wales 28
Eighties Television 30
Advertising – One 32
Science 34
Eighties Idols – Tom Cruise 36
Mix Tape: Opening Lines – Name That Tune 38
Food and Drink 40
Children's Television 42
Eighties Idols – Whitney Houston 44
Famous Film Quotes – One 46
New Wave Pop 48
Eighties Sport – One 50
Power Ballads 52
Eighties Idols – Madonna 54
Back to the Future 56
Eighties Political Quotes 58
Star Wars 60

Sitcoms – One ... 62
Famous Film Quotes – Two ... 64
E.T. the Extra-Terrestrial ... 66
Name The Actress ... 68
Eighties Fashion ... 70
Eighties Sport – Two ... 72
Mix Tape: Opening Lines – Name That Tune – Two ... 74
Sitcoms – Two ... 76
Eighties Game Shows ... 78
Eighties Sport – Three ... 80
Eighties Soap Operas ... 82
Fads and Crazes ... 84
Eighties Idols – Prince ... 86
Famous TV catchphrases ... 88
Coronation Street ... 90
One Hit Wonders ... 92
Eighties Panel Games ... 94
The Royal Wedding ... 96
Science Fiction on Television ... 98
Live Aid ... 100
Name the Actor – Films ... 102
Alternative Comedy ... 104
Advertising – Two ... 106
The King of Pop: Michael Jackson ... 108
Characters in the Eighties – Eastenders ... 110
Blackadder ... 112
ANSWERS ... 114

1. Which international currency was declared legal tender on 22nd February?

2. Name the iconic four-wheel drive sporting coupé that was released by Audi on 3rd March.

3. On 4th March, Robert Mugabe was elected Prime Minister of which African country?

4. Between 8–16th March, an event called 'The Spring Rhythms. Tbilisi-80' was held. It was the first official what in the Soviet Union?

5. Following the taking of American hostages the previous year, The United States cut off diplomatic relations and began economic sanctions against which country on 7th April?

6. Name the Irish singer-songwriter who was born on 11th April and rose to fame as a member of the Irish boyband Westlife.

7. On 14th April, which film starring Dustin Hoffman and Meryl Streep won the Academy Award for Best Picture?

8. On 5th May, the British Special Air Service rescued 20 hostages from a property in South Kensington, London. What was its name?

9. Name the volcano in Washington that erupted on 18th May, killing 57 and causing US$3 billion in damage.

10. The world's first 24-hour news channel was launched in The United States on 1st June. What was its name?

11. On 9th July, seven people were crushed to death in a crowd in Brazil during the visit of which iconic world figure?

12. On 27th July, the politician Mohammad Reza Pahlavi died in Cairo, Egypt. He was the recently deposed pro-Western leader of which country?

13. On 7th August, strikes began at the Gdańsk Shipyard in Poland, led by which charismatic trade unionist?

14. On 5th September, The St. Gotthard Tunnel – the world's longest highway tunnel – opened in which mountainous Central European country?

15. On 10th October, British Prime Minister Margaret Thatcher made a speech in the House of Commons and used the famous line 'The ______ not for ________'.

16. Who announced his resignation as leader of the British Labour Party on 15th October?

17. On 27th October, six Provisional Irish Republican Army prisoners began a hunger strike in which prison in Northern Ireland?

18. Name the English singer-songwriter who was shot dead outside his New York apartment on 8th December.

19. Name the American businessman and founder of a famous fast food restaurant chain who died on 16th December.

20. Which country became the world's largest car producer this year?

THE YEAR THAT WAS 1981

1. In February, there was public outcry after British Telecom announced that all the red telephone boxes would be repainted what colour?
2. On 1st March, the former commanding officer of the Provisional Irish Republican Army began the hunger strike that would kill him 66 days later. What was his name?
3. Name the repressive military dictator who began another 8-year term as President of Chile on 11th March.
4. On 29th March, which sporting event was held for the first time, with 7,500 participants?
5. On 30th March, John Hinckley, Jr. attempted to murder a prominent public figure. Which Hollywood actress was he trying to impress?
6. On 4th April, the British pop group Bucks Fizz won the Eurovision Song Contest with which song?

7. From 10–12th April, 5,000 people took part in riots in which area of South London?

8. Name the iconic 36-year-old singer-songwriter who died of cancer on 11th May.

9. On 13th May, a Turkish gunman named Mehmet Ali Ağca attempted to murder which public figure?

10. Who became the President of France on 21st May?

11. On 22nd May, a 34-year-old man was sentenced to life imprisonment on 13 counts of murder and 7 of attempted murder. What was his name?

12. During the Sri Lankan civil war, a vitally important cultural building at Jaffna was burned by the Tamil United Liberation Front on 1st June. What was it?

13. On 21st July, the England Cricket Team beat Australia at Headingley to win the third Ashes Test. How was this victory unprecedented in the twentieth century?

14. What event attracted a worldwide television audience of over 700 million people on 29th July?

15. MTV launched on 1st August. It was the world's first what?

16. Which popular British BBC sitcom aired for the first time on 8th September?

17. Who performed a free concert in New York's Central Park to an estimated audience of 500,000 on 19th September?

18. Name the Egyptian president who was assassinated during a parade on 6th October.

19. On 12th November, The Church of England General Synod voted in favour of what?

20. Name the heavyweight boxer who lost to Trevor Berbick in Nassau, Bahamas on 11th December, his last fight.

1. On 11th January, who went missing for three days in the Sahara during the Paris-Dakar rally?
2. On 26th January, the post-war record number of 3,070,621 hit the UK headlines. What did it represent?
3. On 30th January, the 'Elk Cloner' was discovered – the first of its kind in the world. What was it?
4. On 3rd March, Queen Elizabeth II opened a performing arts centre in the City of London. What was it called?
5. On 29th March, which British film starring Ben Cross and Ian Charleson won the Academy Award for Best Picture?
6. Which war began on 2nd April?
7. Name the Argentine cruiser that was sunk by the British nuclear submarine HMS *Conqueror* on 2nd May.
8. Which French-Canadian racing driver was killed during qualifying for the Belgian Grand Prix on 8th May?

9. On 26th May, which British football team beat Bayern Munich 1–0 to win the European Cup?

10. Kielder Water, an artificial lake, was opened on 26th May, in which county in North East England?

11. Which European country became the 16th member of NATO on 30th May and the first to join since 1955?

12. On 13th June, the FIFA World Cup began in which country?

13. Which member of the British Royal Family was born on 21st June at St Mary's Hospital in Paddington, West London?

14. Name the son of a Welsh coal miner who was elected Leader of the Social Democratic Party in the UK on 2nd July?

15. Name the unemployed decorator who broke into Buckingham Palace on the morning of 9th July and entered the bedroom of Queen Elizabeth II.

16. Which digital data storage format went on sale to the public for the first time on 17th August in Germany?

17. On 19th September, American computer scientist Scott Fahlman posted a three-character sequence on a message board at Carnegie Mellon to denote a joke. It was the first what?

18. On 1st October, In Orlando, Florida, Walt Disney World opened the EPCOT Center. What does the acronym stand for?

19. On 11th October, the carrack-type warship *The Mary Rose* was raised from the Solent. It was the flagship for which English monarch?

20. On 30th November, the biggest selling album of all time was released. What was its name?

The Year That Was

1983

1. On 3rd January, Kīlauea, a shield volcano began a slow eruption that continues today. Name the island on which it is located.
2. On 24th January, 25 members of the Red Brigades were sentenced to life imprisonment for the 1978 murder of which Italian Christian Democratic politician?
3. What motor safety device became compulsory for drivers and front seat passengers in the United Kingdom on 31st January?
4. On 6th February, the former Nazi SS-Hauptsturmführer nicknamed 'The Butcher of Lyon' was charged with war crimes. What was his name?
5. On 4th April, NASA's second space shuttle made its maiden flight. What was its name?
6. On 15th April, Disneyland opened in which capital city?
7. On 6th May, *Stern* magazine published which notorious forgery?

8. On 13th June, which space probe became the first human-made object to pass Neptune?

9. What first did American physicist Sally Ride achieve on 18th June?

10. Nintendo released the Famicom in Japan on 15th July. How was it more commonly known after it went on sale in Europe three years later?

11. On 22nd July, Australian Dick Smith successfully completed the first solo flight around the world in what type of flying machine?

12. On 18th September, which American heavy metal band appeared on MTV without makeup for the first time?

13. On 25th September, the largest prison escape in British history took place from which prison?

14. On 2nd October, Neil Kinnock became the new Labour Party leader. Who was elected as his deputy?

15. On 12th October, Japan's former Prime Minister Kakuei Tanaka was found guilty of taking a $2 million bribe from which American aerospace company?

16. On 21st October, at the 17th General Conference on Weights and Measures, what unit of measure was defined as the distance light travels in a vacuum in 1/299,792,458 of a second?

17. Which Caribbean island nation did American troops invade on 25th October?

18. On 26th November, £26 million of gold bullion was stolen in the Brink's-Mat robbery. Where was the vault located?

19. Which famous sporting trophy was stolen from a building in Rio de Janeiro on 19th December?

20. McDonald's introduced which iconic food item to its menu?

1. Which oil rich British protectorate in Southeast Asia gained independence from the United Kingdom on 1st January?
2. On 1st February, the British government signed an agreement with which car company, allowing foreign cars to be built in the UK for the first time?
3. A walkout in the village of Brampton Bierlow in South Yorkshire on 6th March marked the beginning of which year-long industrial dispute?
4. On 1st April, which American soul singer was shot dead by his father on the eve of his 45th birthday?
5. On 4th April, which world leader called for a worldwide ban on chemical weapons?
6. Which English comedian died of a heart attack on the TV programme *Live From Her Majesty's* on 15th April?
7. On 22nd April, Britain cut diplomatic relations with Libya following the shooting of which police constable?
8. On 5th May, which country won the Eurovision Song Contest with the song 'Diggi-Loo, Diggi-Ley'?

9. On 14th May, which American computer programmer and billionaire Internet entrepreneur was born in White Plains, New York?

10. Now the largest theatrical producer in the world with over 5,000 employees and an annual turnover of C$850 million, which Canadian entertainment company was formed by two former street-performers on 12th June?

11. On 25th July, Svetlana Savitskaya became the first woman to perform what?

12. On 28th July, The Summer Olympics began in which city?

13. On 5th September, NASA's third space shuttle completed its maiden voyage. What was its name?

14. On 18th September, retired United States Air Force Colonel, Joe Kittinger, completed the first solo Atlantic crossing using what means?

15. On 4th October, mountaineers Tim Macartney-Snape and Greg Mortimer became the first Australians to do what?

16. On 11th October, American geologist Kathryn D. Sullivan became the first American woman to do what?

17. On 12th October, what took place at the Grand Hotel in Brighton?

18. Which world leader was assassinated on 31st October?

19. On 25th November, Band Aid recorded the charity single 'Do They Know It's Christmas?' to raise money for which cause?

20. On 3rd December, the worst industrial disaster in history took place: a leak from a Union Carbide pesticide plant killed more than 23,000 people in which city in Madhya Pradesh, India?

THE YEAR THAT WAS 1985

1. The Waterside Inn at Bray, Berkshire became the first restaurant in the UK to receive three Michelin Guide stars. Name the pair of siblings who founded the establishment.
2. On 10th January, a battery-powered tricycle called the Sinclair C5 was launched. What was its maximum speed: 15 mph, 45 mph or 65 mph?
3. On 17th January, what did British Telecom announce it was going to scrap?
4. On 23rd January, what technical development became operational in the House of Lords for the first time?
5. Name the British civil servant who resigned from the Ministry of Defence on 16th February after leaking documents concerning the sinking of an Argentine navy warship during the Falklands War.
6. Name the BBC1 soap opera that aired for the first time on 19th February.
7. On 13th March, rioting broke out during an FA Cup quarter-final at the Kenilworth Road Stadium. Which team was Luton Town FC playing at home that day?
8. On 23rd April, a successful global brand made a grave marketing error by replacing its original formula with what?

9. On 16th May, scientists of the British Antarctic Survey discovered what stratospheric phenomenon?

10. On 29th May, 39 people died and hundreds were injured when 'supporters' of Liverpool FC attacked fans of which European team at the Heysel Stadium in Brussels?

11. Name the British child prodigy who gained a starred first class degree in Mathematics from the University of Oxford on 4th July at the age of 13.

12. Name the Greenpeace vessel that was bombed and sunk in Auckland Harbour by French DGSE agents on 10th July.

13. On 13th July, the Live Aid pop concert was watched live by an estimated global audience of 1.9 billion. In which two cities was it held?

14. What did a joint Franco-American expedition led by Robert Ballard discover off the coast of Newfoundland on 1st September?

15. Name the policeman who was fatally stabbed on 6th October during the Broadwater Farm Riot in Tottenham, London.

16. Which Manchester United forward was born in Croxteth, Liverpool on 24th October?

17. In Coventry on 28th October, production began of a small European family hatchback – the first foreign car to be built in the UK. What was it?

18. Name the Russian prodigy who defeated Anatoly Karpov on 9th November to become the youngest ever undisputed winner of the World Chess Championship.

19. What treaty was signed at Hillsborough Castle in County Down on 15th November?

20. Name the British charity that was launched live on Noel Edmonds' *Late, Late Breakfast Show* on BBC1 on 25th December?

The Year That Was

1986

1. Name the Conservative Defence Secretary who resigned on 9th January over the Westland affair.
2. On 20th January, The United Kingdom and France announced joint plans to construct what?
3. On 4th March, Britain's first full-colour newspaper was launched. What was it called?
4. On Thursday 13th March, the front page headline of *The Sun* newspaper made a sensational allegation about Freddie Starr. What was it?
5. On 19th March, Buckingham Palace announced the engagement of which royal couple?
6. On 25th March, which film starring Robert Redford and Meryl Streep won the Academy Award for Best Picture?

7. Name the BBC journalist who was kidnapped by Islamic Jihad terrorists in Beirut on 17th April and spent more than five years in captivity.

8. On 5th May, which team did Liverpool FC beat 1–0 to win the Football League First Division title for a record 16th time?

9. Which actor and star of the *Twilight* films was born in London on 13th May?

10. Name the stop-motion clay animation children's series set in the South Pole that premiered in Switzerland on 28th May?

11. On 12th June, Austin Rover was renamed the Rover Group. What was its name four years earlier?

12. In June, which British player won the Golden Boot at the FIFA World Cup in Mexico, shortly before his move to FC Barcelona?

13. On 8th September, Margaret Thatcher officially opened a car factory in Sunderland, owned by which foreign carmaker?

14. On 12th October, Queen Elizabeth II became the first British monarch to visit which country?

15. Name the soap opera that debuted on BBC1 on 27th October, 19 months after its launch in its country of origin.

16. Which 117-mile British motorway did Margaret Thatcher open on 29th October, 11 years after construction began?

17. On 21st November, the government launched a £20 million campaign to warn about what?

18. On 1st December, the government launched an inquiry into a share trading fraud concerning which brewery?

19. Which British utility company was floated on the Stock Exchange on 8th December?

20. Syrian secret agent, Nezar Hindawi, was sentenced to 45 years in prison – the longest fixed jail term imposed by an English court. What was his crime?

The Year That Was

1987

1. On 3rd January, which American singer became the first woman to be inducted into the Rock and Roll Hall of Fame?

2. On 13th January, which member of The Royal Family quit the Royal Marines just three months after joining?

3. On 20th January, the special envoy to the Archbishop of Canterbury in Lebanon was kidnapped in Beirut. What was his name?

4. Which British politician caused widespread offence on 12th February by declaring 'good Christians won't get AIDS'?

5. Name the cross-channel ferry that capsized off Zeebrugge harbour in Belgium on 6th March, killing 193 people.

6. Which long-running cartoon series premiered in the US on 19th April as a series of shorts on *The Tracey Ullman Show*?

7. Which British tennis player was born in Glasgow, Scotland on 15th May?

8. On 22nd May, New Zealand played Italy in the first ever what?

9. Where did eighteen-year-old West German pilot Mathias Rust illegally land his plane on 28th May?

10. On 11th July, the United Nations estimated that the world population had reached how many billion people?

11. On 31st July, Queen Elizabeth II formally opened the country's first driverless railway. What was its name?

12. On 19th August, Michael Ryan killed 16 people in random shootings in which market town in Berkshire?

13. On 7th September, Pink Floyd released their first album without Roger Waters. What was its name?

14. Which foreign retailer opened its first British store at Warrington in Cheshire on 1st October?

15. On the night of 15th October, a violent cyclone caused widespread damage over much of England killing 23 people and felling how many trees: 6 million, 15 million or 45 million?

16. What was the name given to the sharp stock market fall on Wall Street and around the world on 19th October?

17. What did the pilot of a British Aerospace Harrier jet accidentally do on 22nd October?

18. Name the sportsman who was jailed for three years on 23rd October for tax evasion.

19. On 18th November, 31 people died and 100 were injured by a fire at which London Underground Station?

20. Which version of its operating environment Windows did Microsoft release on 9th December?

1. Which large French family car went on sale in the UK on 22nd January and was voted European Car of the Year for 1988?

2. In February, £15 million was raised by the first BBC Telethon for Comic Relief. What was the event called?

3. What item – featuring Sir Isaac Newton – was finally withdrawn from circulation in March?

4. A report released on 9th March revealed that the average price of a house in Britain at the end of the previous year had risen to: £47,000, £60,000 or £120,000?

5. On 10th March, which member of the Royal Family narrowly avoided being caught up in an avalanche during a holiday in Klosters in Switzerland?

6. Who became the first British winner of the US Masters Golf Tournament on 10th April?

7. Name the comic actor and star of 26 *Carry On* films who died on 15th April?

8. Following a series of strikes, on 21st April the government announced a 15 per cent pay rise for which group of public sector workers?

9. Name the French-Canadian female singer who won The Eurovision Song Contest, representing Switzerland on 30th April.

10. Which top-selling English recording artist and BRIT School graduate was born in Tottenham, London on 5th May?

11. On 14th May, which relative newcomers to the Football League beat Liverpool 1–0 at Wembley to win the FA Cup?

12. Which weekly magazine focusing on celebrity news was launched in the UK on 17th May?

13. On 11th June, 80,000 people attended a concert at Wembley Stadium in honour of which imprisoned human rights activist?

14. In July, 'The Freeze' art exhibition was held at Surrey Docks in London, organised by a student at Goldsmiths College of Art. What was his name?

15. On 6th July, 167 workers died when an oil rig in the North Sea exploded. What was its name?

16. Name the 21-year-old midfielder who joined Tottenham Hotspur on 18th July, becoming the first £2 million signing by a British club.

17. On 12th October, who interrupted Pope John Paul II's address to the European Parliament, by shouting, 'I denounce you as the Antichrist!'?

18. On 30th November, which former British Prime Minister unveiled a bronze statue of Clement Attlee outside Limehouse Library in London?

19. Why did Edwina Currie resigns as Health minister on 16th December?

20. One-third of which national park in the United States was destroyed by fires and drought?

THE YEAR THAT WAS 1989

1. On 25th January, John Cleese won a libel case against the *Daily Mirror*. What had the newspaper done wrong?
2. The first satellite television service in Britain launched on 5th February. What was its name?
3. Which British author went into hiding and adopted the pseudonym 'Joseph Anton'?
4. On 23rd February, in an episode of *EastEnders*, the character Den Watts (played by Leslie Grantham) fell into a canal after being shot. How had the assailant concealed the gun?
5. On 4th May, Margaret Thatcher became the first British Prime Minister of the 20th century to do what?
6. On 24th May, who was awarded £600,000 in High Court damages against the satirical magazine *Private Eye*?
7. In China in June, the 'Unknown Rebel' became famous throughout the world for his brave act of defiance. What did he do?

8. Which Hollywood star and giant of twentieth century British theatre, died at his home near Steyning, West Sussex on 11th July?

9. Which star of the *Harry Potter* films was born in West London on 23rd July?

10. What was introduced on 17th August to monitor offenders?

11. On 31st August, Buckingham Palace announced the separation of which royal married couple?

12. On 26th September, Nigel Lawson resigned as Chancellor of the Exchequer. Who replaced him in the post?

13. On 19th October, one woman and three men walked free after the High Court quashed their 1975 convictions for IRA pub bombings. How were they collectively known?

14. Twenty-eight years after its construction, what officially opened on 9th November, 1989?

15. What happened in The House of Commons for the first time in its history on 21st November?

16. Who became Britain's first £1million goalkeeper when he signed with Crystal Palace on 21st November?

17. Which long-running science fiction children's programme was mothballed by the BBC on 6th December after a 26-year run?

18. Name the clay animation film in which the characters Wallace and Gromit made their debut appearance.

19. Permanent security gates were erected across which London street?

20. What was Britain's best-selling car for the eighth year running?

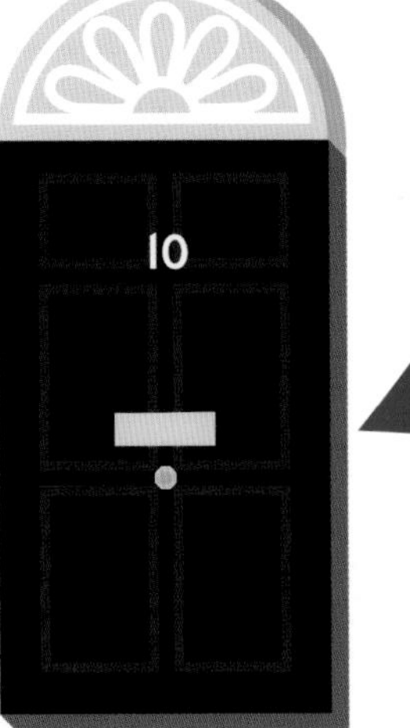

Name the Authors of These Classic Eighties Novels

1. *Waterland*
2. *Love in the Time of Cholera*
3. *Oranges Are Not The Only Fruit*
4. *A Case of Knives*
5. *Contact*
6. *Schindler's Ark*
7. *Empire of the Sun*
8. *The Wasp Factory*
9. *Earthly Powers*
10. *Beloved*
11. *Changes*
12. *Lincoln: A Novel*
13. *The Restaurant at the End of the Universe*
14. *The House of the Spirits*
15. *V for Vendetta*
16. *The Silence of the Lambs*
17. *London Fields*
18. *The Colour of Magic*
19. *Hawksmoor*
20. *An Indecent Obsession*

21. *The Sicilian*
22. *Watchmen*
23. *Sour Sweet*
24. *The Colour Purple*
25. *Small World*
26. *The Tommyknockers*
27. *The Fourth Protocol*
28. *The Satanic Verses*
29. *Firestarter*
30. *The Pillars of the Earth*
31. *Clear and Present Danger*
32. *The Unbearable Lightness of Being*
33. *The Russia House*
34. *Neuromancer*
35. *Blow Your House Down*
36. *Hotel du Lac*
37. *The Alchemist*
38. *A Confederacy of Dunces*
39. *A History of the World in 10½ Chapters*
40. *Hollywood Wives*
41. *The Good Apprentice*
42. *The Bonfire of the Vanities*
43. *Perfume: The Story of a Murderer*
44. *Mistral's Daughter*
45. *A Prayer for Owen Meany*
46. *The Bourne Identity*
47. *The White Hotel*
48. *The Remains of the Day*
49. *The Name of the Rose*
50. *The Handmaid's Tale*

Diana PRINCESS OF WALES

1. She grew up in a rented house on an estate. What was it called?
2. How many siblings did she grow up with?
3. How old was she when her parents divorced?
4. When she was thirteen, what title did she acquire after her father inherited the title of Earl Spencer?

5. She was not an academic child. How many times did she fail her 'O' Levels?

6. Who was 29-year-old Prince Charles dating when he first met sixteen-year-old Diana in 1977?

7. What happened on 6th February 1981 when Diana was nineteen?

8. What job was Diana doing before she got married?

9. Diana was the first what to marry an heir to the British throne since 1659?

10. After their 'fairytale wedding' the happy couple set up home in which two residences?

11. What was officially announced on 5th November, 1981?

12. What did Charles want to call their first child?

13. During the mid-eighties Prince Charles resumed his affair with which now-married former girlfriend?

14. Which former household cavalry officer with whom Diana had a five-year extra-marital affair has been linked with the persistent false rumour that he, not Prince Charles, is the biological father of Prince Harry?

15. Diana's important work with HIV/AIDS sufferers in the 1980s helped to de-stigmatize the disease, but which disapproving member of The Royal Family suggested she focus on 'something more pleasant'?

16. From 1989, she was the president of which hospital?

17. From what illness did Princess Diana suffer?

18. What nickname did Diana give to Camilla Parker-Bowles?

19. What did Camilla call Diana: 'the daft cow', 'that ridiculous creature' or 'Barf Simpson' ?

20. How tall was Diana?

1. Who shot JR: Sue Ellen, Kristin Shepard or Cliff Barnes?
2. Which fictional television character wore a sheepskin jacket and smoked Castella Panatella cigars?
3. Who played the character Juliet Bravo?
4. Which drug-busting American cop drama received an unprecedented 15 Emmy Award nominations for its first season?
5. In the American crime drama series *Magnum, P.I.*, Higgins' highly trained Doberman Pinschers were named after which two Olympian gods?
6. Name the show in which Sorrell Booke played the white-suited commissioner, Boss Hogg.
7. Which American import made ten-year-old Gary Coleman famous, along with his character's catchphrase 'What'chu talkin' 'bout, Willis'?
8. In which American city is the bar in *Cheers*, 'where everybody knows your name'?
9. The motorcycle police series *CHiPs* ran from 1977 to 1983 for 139 episodes during which time neither Frank Llewellyn 'Ponch' Poncherello (Erik Estrada) or Jonathan 'Jon' Baker (Rick Rosner) did what?

10. Name the American action-adventure television series that followed the adventures of a former United States Army Special Forces unit on the run from a crime they didn't commit.

11. What was Jeremy Beadle's Candid Camera style practical joke show called?

12. Name the comedy-drama series that starred Cybill Shepherd and Bruce Willis as private detectives Maddie Hayes and David Addison?

13. Which Evelyn Waugh novel was broadcast on ITV in 11 episodes from 12th October 1981?

14. Who played Hollywood stuntman Colt Seavers in *The Fall Guy*?

15. Which TV detective drove a red 1949 convertible Triumph Roadster?

16. Debbie Allen was nominated for the Emmy Award for Best Actress four times for her role as teacher Lydia Grant in which American television series?

17. Name the ITV crime drama that starred Michael Brandon and Glynis Barber as a crime-busting duo who worked for SI 10, an elite armed unit of the London Metropolitan Police.

18. Which forward-looking BBC television series was hosted during the eighties by Kieran Prendiville, Maggie Philbin, Peter Macann, Michael Rodd, Su Ingle and Howard Stableford?

19. Name the American Emmy Award-winning comedy-drama that ran from 1988 to 1993 and starred Fred Savage and Danica McKellar as Kevin and Winnie.

20. Tyne Daly and Sharon Gless starred as New York City police detectives Christine Cagney and Mary Beth Lacey from 1982 to 1988. Who played who?

1. A television advert that first aired in 1983 featured the actor Norman Lumsden trying to locate a copy of his book, *Fly Fishing*. What product did it advertise?

2. What was the name of the Glade product advertised by the English actress Jenny Logan dancing and singing while vacuuming her living room?

3. Which financial product was memorably parodied in the BBC2 comedy sketch show *Not the Nine O' Clock News* when Pamela Stephenson opened her blouse to reveal her bra?

4. What was advertised by the slogan, 'Full of Eastern Promise'?

5. Which guilt-free luxury was associated with the jingle, 'Only the crumbliest, flakiest chocolate, tastes like chocolate never tasted before'?

6. Name the 1898 Eduardo di Capua composition that inspired the jingle for a popular ice cream advert set in Venice.

7. The Scottish actor Gregor Fisher appeared as his 'Baldy Man' character in a series of adverts for what product?

8. Which company, whose 1985 advert featured the famous theme of 'Re-Record Not Fade Away', offered a lifetime guarantee for its VHS videotapes?

9. Stephen Frost and Mark Arden appeared as a comedy duo in a long-running series of commercials for which brand of lager?

10. Adam Perry and Stelios Havatzias appeared together in one of the most iconic and best-selling Athena posters of all time. What was the shirtless Adam Perry holding?

11. What were, 'tasty, tasty, very, very tasty, they're very tasty'?

12. 'Will it be chips or jacket spuds? Will it be salad or frozen peas? Will it be mushrooms? Fried onion rings? We'll have to wait and see . . . Hope it's chips it's chips, we hope it's chips it's chips . . .' Name the brand and food being advertised.

13. A 1984 advertisement featured a female athlete hurling a sledge-hammer a at a Big Brother-like face on a huge TV screen. What product did it advertise?

14. In an advert based on the film *Raiders of the Lost Ark*, a man is chased down a tunnel by a huge boulder. What was he searching for?

15. Name the model who stripped to his boxer shorts in the laundrette, accompanied by Marvin Gaye's hit 'I Heard It Through The Grapevine'.

16. What was he advertising?

17. What product was advertised by a cartoon of the sun wearing sunglasses and singing the tune of an old hit by Desmond Dekker & The Aces, accompanied by a field of sunflowers?

18. Which frozen convenience food used the slogans, 'Every day has got a different taste', 'They're deliciously different' and 'Success on a plate for you'?

19. What was the catchphrase of the Norfolk turkey farmer, Bernard Matthews?

20. 'Kids will eat it till the cows come home!' Eat what?

Phone Book

SCIENCE

1. In 1980, Microsoft began to develop an operating system for the IBM Personal Computer. What was it called?
2. On 1st March 1980, the *Voyager 1* probe confirmed the existence of Janus, a moon of which planet?
3. In June 1980, Geophysicists Luis and Walter Alvarez with Frank Asaro and Helen Michels proposed the Alvarez hypothesis. What did it posit?
4. What was the name of the first ever manned reusable spacecraft to return to Earth from orbit, in April 1981?
5. What was the name of the British home computer launched by Sinclair Research in March 1981?
6. In January 1982, Commodore International released its best-selling 8-bit home computer. What was its name?
7. On 14th October 1982, which comet was spotted in the sky for the first time in 70 years?

8. Name the British public-service television station that was launched on 2nd November 1982.

9. On 1st January 1983, the ARPANET switched its networking technology to the TCP/IP – marking the official birth of what?

10. In February 1984, Astronauts Bruce McCandless II and Robert L. Stewart performed the first what?

11. On 24th January 1984, the first successful PC to use a graphical user interface was launched. What was its name?

12. In June 1984, in the Soviet Union, Alexey Pajitnov launched his tile-matching video game. What was it called?

13. In 1986, the first confirmed case of which fatal neurodegenerative disease in the UK was reported?

14. On 15th March 1985, a computer systems firm in Cambridge, Massachusetts called Symbolics Inc. registered the first what?

15. On 20th November 1985, Microsoft released its first graphical personal computer operating system. What was it called?

16. On 3rd April 1986, IBM launched the PC Convertible, its first what?

17. In November 1987, a man in Florida became the first person to be convicted with the aid of which genetic technology?

18. Which popular SSRI antidepressant made its debut in the US just after Christmas in 1987?

19. On 1st December 1987, digging began on which Anglo-French construction project?

20. In 1988, Stephen Hawking published a landmark popular-science book. What was its title?

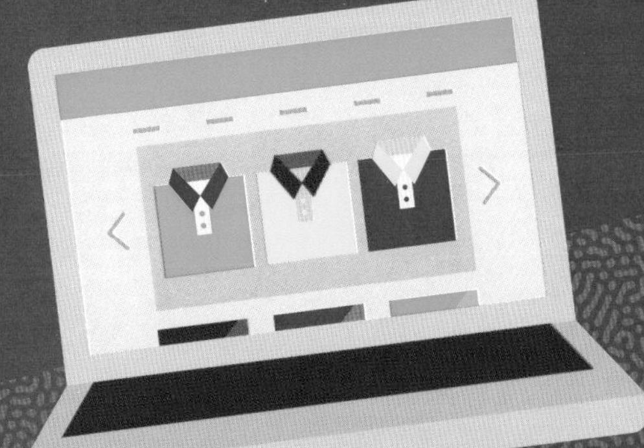

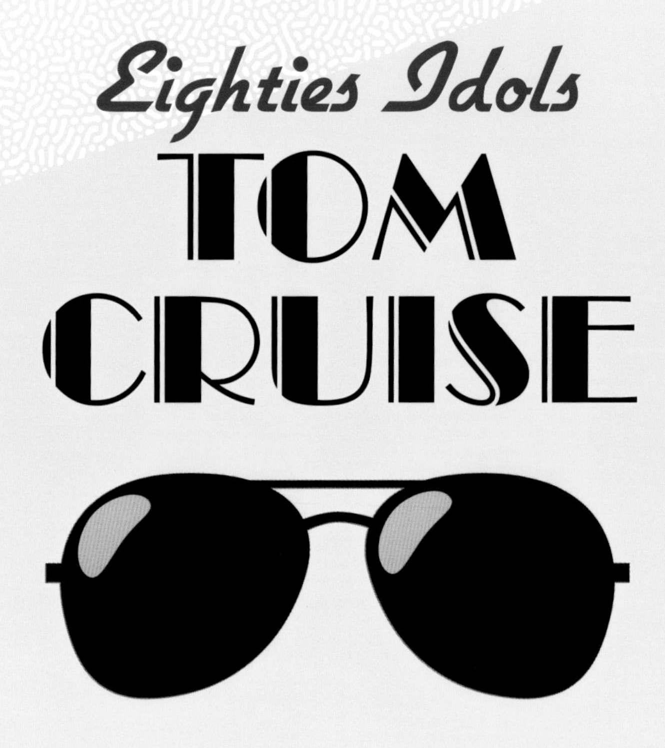

1. In 1981, Tom Cruise's debut film was a romantic drama directed by Franco Zeffirelli and starring Brooke Shields and Martin Hewitt. Diana Ross and Lionel Richie sang the title song. What was the name of the film?

2. In Cruise's second film, *Taps* (1981), a group of military students take over their military academy to stop it from closing. Which future 'dead man walking' made his film debut as Cadet Captain Alex Dwyer?

3. The director of Cruise's third film, *The Outsiders* (1983), only agreed to take on the project because a group of school students sent him a letter asking him to do it. Who was he?

4. In *Losin' It* (1983) Cruise and three friends travelled to Tijuana, Mexico to lose what?

5. In *Risky Business* (1983), Cruise became a major star by dancing in his underpants while wearing a pink shirt. Name the nostalgic Bob Seger song that famously accompanied his antics?

6. How did his father's Porsche 928 get damaged in the film?

7. Which sport provided the backdrop for his next film, *All the Right Moves* (1983)?

8. Cruise's beautiful on-screen girlfriend Lisa also played Marty McFly's mother in the *Back to the Future* trilogy. What was her name?

9. What personal tragedy did Cruise have to face while making *Legend* (1985)?

10. Who directed the film?

11. *Top Gun* was the highest-grossing film of 1986. Which actor didn't want to appear in it, but was forced to by contractual obligations: Tom Cruise, Tim Robbins, Meg Ryan, Kelly McGillis, Val Kilmer or Anthony Edwards?

12. Which of these actors turned down Tom Cruise's role in *Top Gun*: Scott Baio, Matthew Broderick, Nicolas Cage, John Cusack, Emilio Estevez, Michael J. Fox, Tom Hanks, Sean Penn, Patrick Swayze?

13. Cruise's co-star in *The Colour of Money* (1986) won an Academy Award for Best Actor for his role. What was his name?

14. Who directed the film?

15. Name the Australian actor who co-starred in *Cocktail* (1988).

16. Cruise's character dreamed about one day opening his own cocktail bar. What did he plan to call it?

17. What was the name of Cruise's character in *Rain Man* (1988)?

18. Where did Raymond (Dustin Hoffman) always buy his underwear?

19. Who directed *Born on the Fourth of July* (1989)?

20. On which day in July was Tom Cruise actually born?

NAME THAT TUNE

1. 'Clock strikes upon the hour and the sun begins to fade.'
2. 'We're talking away I don't know what I'm to say I'll say it anyway.'
3. 'You must understand though the touch of your hand makes my pulse react.'
4. 'I hear the drums echoing tonight.'
5. 'We're no strangers to love; you know the rules and so do I.'
6. 'Turn around: every now and then I get a little bit lonely and you're never coming round.'
7. 'I know when to go out and when to stay in.'
8. 'Punctured bicycle on a hillside desolate.'
9. 'You are now about to witness the strength of street knowledge.'
10. 'Who's gonna tell you when it's too late?'

11. 'And you can dance for inspiration.'
12. 'It doesn't hurt me, do you wanna feel how it feels?'
13. 'Sometimes you're better off dead.'
14. 'Poor old Johnny Ray sounded sad upon the radio, he moved a million hearts in Mono.'
15. 'That's great, it starts with an earthquake.'
16. 'I pictured a rainbow, you held it in your hands.'
17. 'See the stone set in your eyes, see the thorn twist in your side.'
18. 'It was Christmas Eve babe in the drunk tank.'
19. 'And you may find yourself living in a shotgun shack.'
20. 'A police car and a screaming siren, a pneumatic drill and ripped up concrete.'

FOOD AND Drink

1. What was the name of the low alcohol shandy drink that children could buy in the UK from the 1960s to the 1980s?
2. During the eighties, Lenny Henry advertised a new style of Smiths crisp. What geometric shape was it?
3. Which company produced Pot Noodle during the eighties?
4. What had 'a hazelnut in every bite'?
5. What was advertised on television by a handful of peanuts closing and then opening again to reveal a chocolate bar, with the slogan 'It's so satisfying'?
6. Which margarine was advertised by the slogan, 'Something to feel good about'?
7. Space Raiders – crisps in the shape of an alien head – remained the same price throughout the eighties (and right up to 2007). How much were they?

8. Which savoury biscuit snack by Burton's was sold in packets designed to look like a tabloid newspaper?

9. Which Cadbury product had a milk chocolate covering, was filled with caramel and crushed roasted peanuts and changed its name to Peanut Boost in 1989?

10. Which Rowntree's chocolate bar was marketed during the eighties as the favourite chunky snack for truck drivers?

11. What was the name of the square-shaped chewy fruit sweets with a crunchy sugar shell, sold by Rowntree's?

12. Small pieces of gold bubblegum sold in a tiny hessian bag – what was the product called?

13. Which short-lived chocolate bar was billed as '5 treats to the bar'?

14. 'New! Light crispy wafer plus roast nut flavour'. Name that chocolate bar.

15. Which chocolate treat featured a sexy cartoon rabbit smoothly voiced by Miriam Margolyes – Professor Sprout from the *Harry Potter* films?

16. 'There's no nicer way to eat real milk chocolate than on a ________.'

17. 'Coconut, caramel, cherries and milk chocolate, daylight come and me wanna go home: ________!'

18. It had a creamy mousse centre covered in a bird's nest-style Nestlé chocolate shell. What single word was printed in purple and white letters on its golden wrapper?

19. Which Cadbury's chocolate bar was launched in the UK in 1983 as a competitor to Rowntree's Aero and featured a purple wrapper with red writing?

20. What was the name of the pink foot-shaped strawberry ice cream that was an eighties favourite?

1. Which programme debuted in 1983, featuring three species of mutually dependent creatures: Fraggles, Doozers and Gorgs?
2. Which television family included Grandpa, Father, Mother, Posie, Perkin and Pootle?
3. In which word-puzzle game programme, hosted by Janet Ellis and Adrian Hedley, did the creepy Mr Noseybonk appear?
4. What was the name of Keith Chegwin's game show in which two schools competed as Reds and Yellows, with different celebrity captains each week?
5. Which rapping rodent transformed the fortunes of the ailing British breakfast television show, *TV-AM*?
6. Name the French-Canadian-American animated television series starring a cyborg detective and his evil nemesis, Dr Claw.
7. Who played the rebellious

teenager Suzanne Ross in *Grange Hill* and Michelle Fowler in the BBC soap opera *EastEnders*?

8. Name the superhero alter egos of Prince Adam of Eternia and his sister, Princess Adora.

9. Which two television series used the unforgettable telephone number 01-811 8055: 'oh one, eight double one, eight oh five five'?

10. Who became the youngest ever presenter on *Blue Peter* when she debuted on 29th June 1987, three months before her 19th birthday?

11. In what year in the distant future was Gerry Anderson's 1983 science-fiction television series *Terrahawks* set?

12. Who voiced the eye-patch wearing secret agent animated character, Danger Mouse?

13. Which small blue mushroom-dwelling animated creatures were originally called *Les Schtroumpfs* by their Belgian creator?

14. Which children's television comedy-drama starred Julia Sawalha and Dexter Fletcher as journalists on a school newspaper called the *Junior Gazette*?

15. Name the spin-off series that starred a five-foot-tall robot who first appeared on the ITV children's show *The Saturday Banana*.

16. Which BAFTA-winning natural history programme launched in 1986, presented by Nicola 'Nick' Davies, Terry Nutkins and Chris Packham?

17. Chock-A-Block was a large yellow what?

18. Who hosted the early morning school-holidays programme, *Wacaday*?

19. The Munch Bunch were a group of walking, talking what?

20. Name the burrowing rodent puppet that appeared with Phillip Schofield in the continuity programme *The Broom Cupboard* between 1985 and 1987.

Eighties Idols

WHITNEY HOUSTON

1. Through her mother, Houston was a first cousin of one of the most-charted female vocalists of all time? What was her name?
2. Who taught Whitney how to sing?
3. In 1978, at age 15, Houston sang background vocals on which Chaka Khan hit single?
4. During the early 1980s she became a successful teen model and was the first black woman to feature as the cover model for which American teen magazine?
5. She was offered several recording contracts in her teens but her mother turned them down. Why?
6. In 1983, with which record label did she eventually sign?
7. Her first successful release was a pop ballad duet called 'Hold Me' with which former lead singer of Harold Melvin & the Blue Notes?
8. In February 1985, she released what was to become the best-selling debut album by a solo artist. What was it called?

9. Which ballad from the album reached No.3 in the US Billboard Hot 100 chart and topped the Hot R&B chart?

10. Name the jazzy ballad that became her first No.1 single in both the US and the UK.

11. In which year did she perform The Greatest Love World Tour?

12. The music video for which hit features her dancing in a setting of video screens and coloured partitions?

13. Since its launch in 1981, she was the first African-American woman to receive consistent airplay on which television channel?

14. 'The Greatest Love of All' was a huge hit for Whitney, but it was originally recorded in 1977 by which American singer and jazz guitarist?

15. She won her first Grammy Award for Best Female Pop Vocal Performance for which song?

16. What did she subsequently win for her performance of the song at the televised Grammy Awards?

17. She released her second album in June 1987. What was its title?

18. Which Grammy Award-winning song from the second album begins, 'Clock strikes upon the hour and the sun begins to fade'?

19. What record, previously shared by The Beatles and the Bee Gees did she subsequently surpass?

20. Name the global non-profit fundraising organization that she formed in 1989.

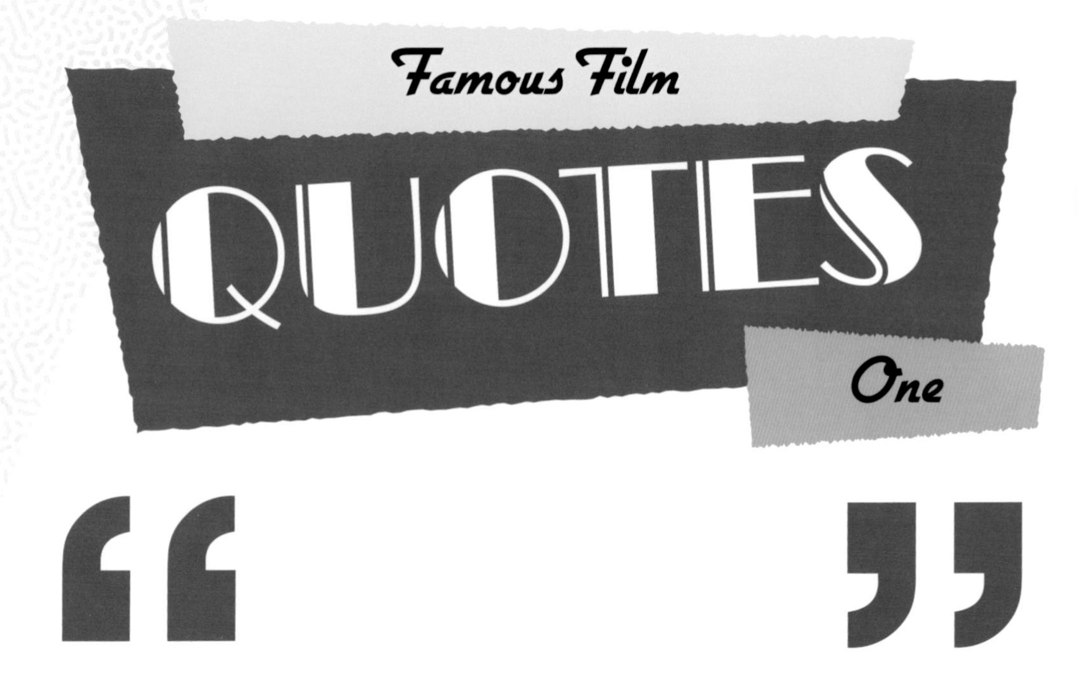

Who Said It and in What Film?

1. 'I have a head for business and a bod for sin. Is there anything wrong with that?'
2. 'It's 106 miles to Chicago, we got a full tank of gas, half a pack of cigarettes, it's dark, and we're wearing sunglasses.'
3. 'When you grow up, your heart dies.'
4. 'If it bleeds, we can kill it.'
5. 'Give my daughter the shot!'
6. 'I've got it. Why don't we spread chocolate all over the floor and let Chunk eat his way through?'
7. 'I just met a wonderful new man. He's fictional, but you can't have everything.'

8. 'This is the cleanest and nicest police car I've ever been in in my life. This thing's nicer than my apartment.'
9. 'That's not a knife. *That's* a knife.'
10. 'I hate snakes, Jock! I hate 'em!'
11. 'Stop . . . that . . . train!'
12. 'I'm not gonna hurt ya. I'm just gonna bash your brains in.'
13. 'These are the simple rules: no barking, no growling, you will not lift your leg to anything in this house.'
14. 'I get so excited when you get angry. It makes me feel so much closer to the reading of the will.'
15. 'Nine million terrorists in the world and I gotta kill one with feet smaller than my sister.'
16. 'Gordon's alive!'
17. 'Every day for the last ten years, Loretta there has been giving me a large black coffee. Today she gives me a large black coffee, only it's got sugar in it. A lot of sugar.'
18. 'Don't push it or I'll give you a war you won't believe. Let it go.'
19. 'And how can this be? For he is the Kwisatz Haderach!'
20. 'You think you have won! What is light without dark? What are you without me? I am a part of you all. You can never defeat me.'

NEW WAVE Pop

1. Released in 1981, *Architecture & Morality* was the third album of which British synthpop band?
2. British post-punk front man Stuart Leslie Goddard is better known by what alliterative stage name?
3. Which pop trio is listed in *The Guinness Book of World Records* as the all-female group with the most chart entries in the world?
4. Only one of Spandau Ballet's hits reached No.1 in the UK singles charts. Was it 'Gold', 'True' or 'Chant No 1 (I Don't Need This Pressure On)'?
5. Formed in Leeds Polytechnic, which synthpop duo had a No.1 hit in 17 countries with a song originally recorded by American singer Gloria Jones in 1964?
6. Which new wave band was named after a character from Roger Vadim's French science-fiction film, *Barbarella*?
7. 'Sax and Violins' was the final release of which post-punk new wave American rock band?

8. The sleeve of which lengthy 1983 hit was simply labelled 'FAC SEVENTY THREE' and cost so much to print that Factory Records made a 5 pence loss on each single?

9. Whose 1981 debut single was entitled 'Dancing with Myself'?

10. The first ever single containing a rap went to No.1 in the UK in 1985. What was its name?

11. Grace Jones's 1985 signature hit 'Slave to the Rhythm' was originally written by Trevor Horn for which of his protégés: Frankie Goes to Hollywood, Pet Shop Boys or Dollar?

12. 'You Spin Me Round (Like a Record)' by British band Dead or Alive was the first UK No.1 hit for which British songwriting and record producing trio?

13. Best known for their 1983 hit 'Hold Me Now', which British new wave group was named after the two shambling detectives in Hergé's comic strip *The Adventures of Tintin*?

14. Which eighties electronic music pioneer changed his stage name from 'Valerian' after spotting an advert in the Yellow Pages?

15. Which androgynous eighties icon occasionally sang with Bow Wow Wow as Lieutenant Lush before forming his own band?

16. In 1983, *The Hurting* peaked at No.1 on the UK Album Chart. It was the debut album for which new wave synthesizer duo?

17. Which eighties frontman rarely appeared without his trademark gold lamé suit?

18. Which chart-topping 1980 hit was a tribute to American R&B singer Geno Washington?

19. 'Wishing (If I Had a Photograph of You)' was a hit for which Liverpool-based synthpop band?

20. The fourth single from The Human League's studio album *Dare* was the 1981 Christmas No.1 in the UK. What was its title?

Eighties SPORT One

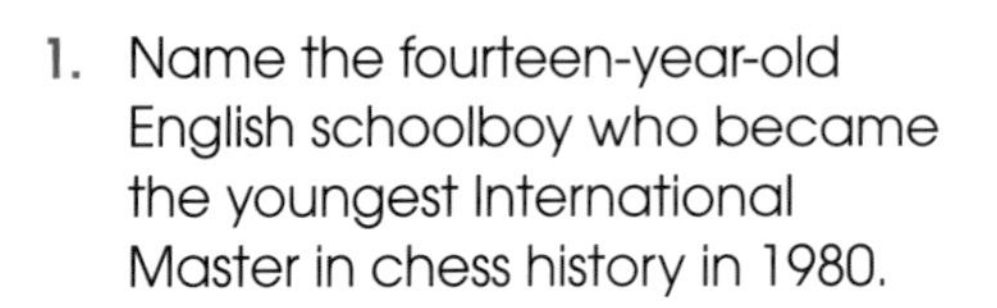

1. Name the fourteen-year-old English schoolboy who became the youngest International Master in chess history in 1980.
2. In the 1988 Summer Olympics, who won gold medals in the long jump and the heptathlon and set the still-standing heptathlon world record of 7,291 points?
3. At the World Matchplay darts championship on 13th October 1984, who won £100,000 for making the first televised 9-dart 501 finish?
4. Who scored a record 346 goals for Liverpool FC between 1980 and 1996?
5. On 11th July 1982, which country beat Germany 3–1 to win the FIFA World Cup in Spain?
6. The rivalry between Sebastian Coe and Steve Ovett was a highlight of the 1980 Olympics. Which final did Ovett win: 800m or 1500m?
7. In May 1985, which team won the FA Cup for the sixth time in its history, by beating Everton 1–0 at Wembley?
8. Who won three gold medals and a silver during the 1988 Summer Olympics and still holds both female world records for 100m and 200m events?

9. In 1984, British skaters Jayne Torvill and Christopher Dean earned a perfect score for their programme in the Sarajevo Winter Olympics. Name the French one-movement orchestral piece that provided their accompaniment.

10. In 1984, who won the long jump Olympic title for the first of four consecutive times?

11. Which English athlete won the decathlon gold medal at the Olympic Games in 1980 and 1984 and broke the world record four times?

12. In 1985, who missed a blue during a potential 147 break and then threw away a 13–8 advantage and the World Snooker Championship to Steve Davis?

13. In which year did 17-year-old Boris Becker become the youngest ever winner of the men's singles at Wimbledon?

14. On 22nd February 1980, which country's hockey team beat the Soviet Union in the semi-finals of the Winter Olympics in 'The Miracle on Ice'?

15. Who famously fell foul of Zola Budd during the 3000m final at the 1984 Olympics?

16. Which British athlete won the 100m silver in the 1988 Olympics with a time of 9.97 seconds?

17. How much was the prize money for the Wimbledon Men's Singles Championship in 1980: £20,000, £200,000 or £2 million?

18. On 19th December 1983, what was special about the league match between Manchester United and Tottenham Hotspur?

19. On12th June 1984, in one of the greatest NBA Finals ever, which team beat the Los Angeles Lakers in 7 games to win their 15th NBA Championship?

20. In 1984, which Australian bowler set a new record of 351 Test wickets?

POWER BALLADS

Match the Hit with Its Singer

1. 'If I Could Turn Back Time'
2. 'Total Eclipse of the Heart'
3. 'China in Your Hand'
4. 'Every Rose Has Its Thorn'
5. 'All Out of Love'
6. 'Dancing in the Dark'
7. 'I Want to Know What Love Is'
8. 'Dead Ringer for Love'
9. 'Hard to Say I'm Sorry'
10. 'Heaven Is a Place On Earth'
11. 'The Power of Love'
12. 'Africa'
13. 'Is This Love'
14. 'The Final Countdown'
15. 'China In Your Hand'
16. 'Livin' on a Prayer"
17. 'Don't Stop Believin''
18. '(I Just) Died In Your Arms'
19. 'Alone'
20. 'Nothing's Gonna Stop Us Now'
21. 'Up Where We Belong'
22. 'Broken Wings'

23. ‘Can’t Fight This Feeling

24. ‘Listen to Your Heart’

25. ‘Drive’

26. ‘We Don’t Need Another Hero’

27. ‘Kayleigh’

28. ‘Holding Out for a Hero’

29. ‘Black Velvet’

30. ‘Against All Odds (Take A Look At Me Now) ’

Air Supply

Alannah Myles

Belinda Carlisle

Bon Jovi

Bonnie Tyler x 2

Bruce Springsteen

Cher

Chicago

Cutting Crew

Europe

Foreigner

Heart

Huey Lewis and the News

Joe Cocker & Jennifer Warnes

Journey

Marillion

Meat Loaf

Mr Mister

Phil Collins

Poison

REO Speedwagon

Roxette

Starship

The Cars

Tina Turner

Toto

T’Pau x 2

Whitesnake

1. While working as a backup singer she played drums and then became lead singer of a band with boyfriend Dan Gilroy. What was it called?

2. She signed a singles deal with Sire Records in 1982 and released her debut single. What was it called?

3. What was the title of her second single, released in March 1983?

4. Her third single became a global hit. What was it called?

5. She became a global star after the release of her second album in November 1984. What was its title?

6. Wearing a pink strapless gown, which Hollywood icon did she mimic in the video for her next hit, 'Material Girl'?

7. Name the Susan Seidelman feature film that gave Madonna her first high profile role?

8. In 1985, a low-budget erotic drama she filmed in 1979 for a fee of $100 was released. What was its title?

9. How did she react to the film's release?

10. Which New York hip-hop band supported her on her first concert tour in North America, The Virgin Tour?

11. In June 1986, her third studio album, *True Blue*, produced three American chart toppers: 'Live to Tell', 'Open Your Heart' and which other?

12. What was the name of the romantic comedy film she made in 1987, which also became the name for her subsequent world tour?

13. Who did she divorce in 1989?

14. In 1989, Pepsi made and cancelled a lucrative endorsement because of which controversial music video?

15. What was the name of her fourth studio album, released in 1989?

16. Which song on the album was a tribute to American funk and soul band Sly and the Family Stone?

17. In the video for 'Express Yourself' Madonna played a chained masochist, with muscular men as her workers. What was the name of the Iranian-born supermodel she singled out at the end for her date?

18. What aphorism appears at the end of the video?

19. Which Madonna song contains the lyrics 'You're just jealous 'cause you can't beat me'?

20. What is Madonna's clothing line predictably called?

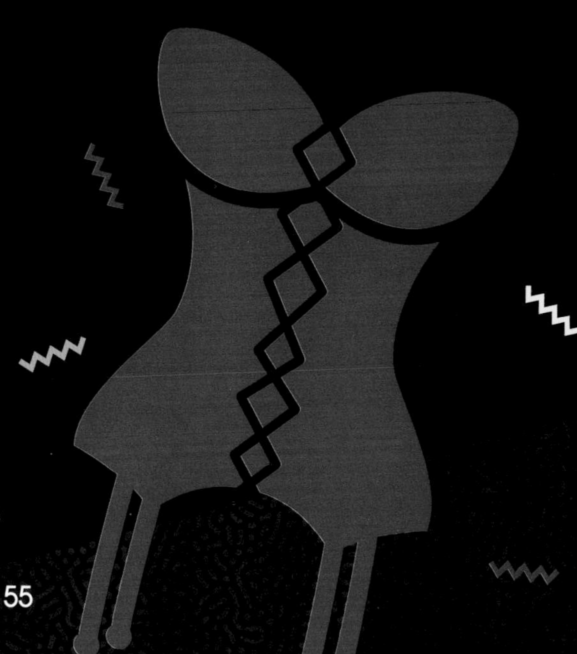

BACK TO THE Future

1. Who played Marty McFly for four weeks of filming before being replaced by Michael J. Fox?
2. The head of Universal Studios didn't like the title *Back To The Future*. What did he suggest as a replacement?
3. To what year did Marty travel back in time?
4. What was Marty's girlfriend called?
5. What speed did the time machine have to reach to enable time travel?
6. Which soft drink brand appeared frequently throughout the film?

7. How did Lorraine and George originally meet?
8. Who made his film debut as the character Match – a member of Biff's gang?
9. What was the name of Doc's pet dog?
10. Which Chuck Berry song did Marty perform at his parents' school dance?
11. How many 'jigowatts' of electricity were needed to start the nuclear reaction in the time machine?
12. Name the core component of the time machine that Doc described as 'what makes time travel possible'?
13. What radioactive chemical element fuelled the reaction?
14. Which Huey Lewis and the News song written for the film was a No.1 hit in the US?
15. What pseudonym did Marty adopt in 1955 because his teenage mother saw it written on his underpants?
16. Whose car in 1955 was a 1950 Packard Super Eight convertible?
17. What was 'Enchantment Under the Sea'?
18. What word appeared on the vanity license plate used on The DeLorean time machine?
19. What nationality were the terrorists from whom Doc stole the fuel?
20. Which actor who starred in the film has since claimed to have only watched it once?

Who Said It?

1. 'Nobody would remember the Good Samaritan if he had only good intentions. He had money as well.'
2. 'I am not interested in a third party. I do not believe it has any future.'
3. 'I foresee a Liberal vote so massive and the number of Liberal MPs so great that we shall hold the initiative in the new Parliament.'
4. 'To those waiting with baited breath for that favourite media catchphrase, the U Turn, I have only one thing to say. You turn if you want to. The Lady's not for turning.'
5. 'It is quite clear to me that the Tory Party will get rid of Mrs Thatcher in about 3 years time.'
6. 'Without false modesty, I don't think I have a fraction of the talent of either Bevan of Foot.'
7. (On his father) 'He didn't riot. He got on his bike and looked for work and he kept looking until he found it.'

8. (On winning the Falklands War) 'We knew what we had to do and we went about it and did it. Great Britain is great again.'

9. 'The longest suicide note in history.' (Describing the 1983 Labour manifesto)

10. 'The idea that the GLC should be abolished at a stroke is ill though out, undemocratic and will cost the people of London dear.'

11. 'If Margaret Thatcher wins on Thursday, I warn you not to be ordinary, I warn you not to be young, I warn you not to fall ill, I want you not to be old.'

12. 'Arthur Scargill is a bloody lunatic.'

13. 'Having served in eleven Parliaments, it would be difficult to describe this as a maiden speech. It would be like Elizabeth Taylor appearing at her next wedding in a white gown.'

14. 'My fellow Americans, I am pleased to tell you that I have signed legislation to outlaw Russia forever. We begin bombing in five minutes.'

15. 'I'm still a loony, dribbling Leftie.'

16. (On Norman Tebbit) 'A loutish Minister of the thuggish tendency.'

17. (On Margaret Thatcher) 'She is a bounder, a liar, a deceiver, a cheat, a crook and a disgrace to the House of Commons.'

18. 'Mrs (Edwina) Currie loses an enormous number of opportunities to remain silent.'

19. 'There is no such thing as society. There are individual men and women, and there are families.'

20. 'There has always been, and there always will be, an economic cycle.'

STAR WARS

1. During development what was Luke Skywalker originally called?
2. What did 20th Century Fox agree to give director George Lucas instead of a large salary – representing one of the biggest mistakes in film history?
3. In early drafts of the screenplay, which character was originally called Buffy?
4. Which role did Anthony Daniels play?
5. Which role did Kenny Baker play?
6. What spacecraft had to be redesigned at short notice because the original model too closely resembled one from the 1970s British TV series *Space: 1999*?

7. Which character came from the planet Kashyyyk?

8. True or false: before it was decided to use animatronics for Yoda, he was nearly played by a performing monkey.

9. Which of these actors was considered for the part of Han Solo: Tom Selleck, Kurt Russell, Christopher Walken, Sylvester Stallone, Al Pacino?

10. How many times was the word 'ewok' uttered in the *Star Wars* films?

11. R2D2 was named after what?

12. How much was Harrison Ford paid for his performance in the first film: $10,000, $100,000 or $1,000,000?

13. What was the home planet of C-3PO?

14. What inspired the shape of the Millennium Falcon?

15. Jawaese (spoken by Jawas) was based on a speeded-up version of which African language?

16. Who directed *The Empire Strikes Back*?

17. Which character was nearly dressed in a pair of baggy shorts because studio executives felt he was too naked?

18. Which *Star Wars* actor dismissed the films as 'fairy-tale rubbish'?

19. Which pioneering actor/director did George Lucas originally want for the voice of Darth Vader before deciding he was too recognisable?

20. Who earned millions for 4.5 hours work on *The Empire Strikes Back* after demanding a quarter of one per cent of the film's total gross?

1. In which sitcom did Lynda Baron play Nurse Gladys Emmanuel?

2. Who sang the theme tune for *A Fine Romance?*

3. Which sitcom was broadcast on BBC1 from 1979 to 1987 and centred around a middle-class couple living in Purley?

4. Which English television writer devised and wrote *The Liver Birds, Butterflies* and *Bread*?

5. Name the sitcom written by the creators of *Birds of a Feather* and *Goodnight Sweetheart* that starred Rik Mayall as Alan B'Stard MP.

6. What was the name of Paul Eddington's character in *Yes Minister*?

7. Who played Leonard 'Oz' Osborne in *Auf Wiedersehen, Pet*?

8. The British television sitcom, *Rings on Their Fingers,* starred Martin Jarvis and which star of seventies sitcom *The Cuckoo Waltz* and, more recently, the British TV drama *Doctors* (as Julia Parsons)?

9. Which sitcom featured a running gag about 'The Fallen Madonna with the Big Boobies'?

10. Which Channel 4 sitcom was set in a barbershop in Peckham, South East London?

11. Name the longest-running sitcom in the world.

12. Which BBC sitcom featured the 'children' Joey, Jack, Adrian, Aveline and Billy?

13. Which sitcom was set in Chigwell, Essex and starred three main characters with the surnames Green, Stubbs and Theodopolopodos?

14. Name the Scottish sitcom in which bank teller Willie Melvin dreamt of being a successful writer.

15. *Are You Being Served?* ran until 1985. In which year did it begin?

16. What was the name of the fictional holiday camp in *Hi-de-Hi!*?

17. Which BBC sitcom was centred around Flat 127, Nelson Mandela House?

18. Which BBC1 sitcom ran to four series, each set in a different historical period: medieval, Elizabethan, Regency and the early twentieth century?

19. Who played the titular demobbed RAF serviceman Harvey, in *Shine on Harvey Moon*?

20. The surnames of Ralph, Gertude and Edward formed the title of which short-lived 1987 sitcom?

FAMOUS FILM Quotes Two

Who Said It and in What Film?

1. 'I love that it takes you an hour and a half to order a sandwich.'
2. 'Life moves pretty fast. You don't stop and look around once in a while, you could miss it.'
3. 'Get away from her, you bitch!'
4. 'I am serious ... and don't call me Shirley.'
5. 'I've seen things you people wouldn't believe. Attack ships on fire off the shoulder of Orion.'

6. 'Say hello to my little friend.'
7. 'He slimed me.'
8. 'Alright, alright, Mickey's a mouse, Donald's a duck, Pluto's a dog. What's Goofy?'
9. 'I am not an animal! I am a human being.'
10. 'They're here.'
11. 'Wax on, right hand. Wax off, left hand.'
12. 'I feel the need. The need for speed.'
13. 'Roads? Where we're going we don't need roads.'
14. 'No. I am your father.'
15. 'Excellent!'
16. 'I'm an excellent driver.'
17. 'Be afraid, be very afraid.'
18. 'Nobody puts Baby in a corner.'
19. 'Is it you?'
20. 'Don't you do it! Don't ... you ... I got nowhere else to go! I got nowhere else to go! I ain't got nothin' else.'

1. Which year was *E.T. the Extra-Terrestrial* released in the UK: 1981, 1982, 1983 or 1984?
2. What was Elliot's dog called?
3. What confectionery did Elliot leave on the floor to lure E.T. into his bedroom?
4. Whilst alone at home, what food did E.T. sample first from the fridge and then throw on the floor?
5. What was the first phrase that E.T. spoke?
6. Why did Elliot release all the frogs in his biology class?
7. How did E.T. learn to speak English?
8. On Halloween, how did Michael and Elliott disguise E.T. so they could sneak him out of the house?

9. What costume did Gertie wear on Halloween?

10. What type of flower did E.T. bring back to life?

11. What electronic toy did E.T. modify to build a transmitter so that he could 'phone home'?

12. How did Elliot convince his mother that he was too sick to go to school?

13. Instead of actors, who did Spielberg hire to play the doctors in the emergency medical scenes?

14. How did Elliot and E.T. escape a police roadblock while racing on a bike to the forest?

15. What gender was E.T.?

16. For the first half of the film, who was shot only from the waist down?

17. How did Spielberg shoot the film to allow the child actors greater emotional continuity?

18. Who composed the film's musical score?

19. It was the highest-grossing film of all time and held this record until 1993 when it was overtaken by which other Spielberg blockbuster?

20. The film was nominated for nine Oscars, including Best Picture and Best Director, but lost both to which film?

ACTRESS

Name the Actress in Both Films

1. *Nine to Five* (1980), *On Golden Pond* (1981)
2. *Star Wars: Episode VI – Return of the Jedi* (1983), *Hannah and Her Sisters* (1986)
3. *Blade Runner* (1982), *Wall Street* (1987)
4. *Splash* (1984), *Roxanne* (1987)
5. *This Is Spinal Tap* (1984), *Prizzi's Honour* (1985)
6. *Ghostbusters* (1984), *Gorillas in the Mist* (1988)
7. *Once Upon a Time in America* (1984), *She's Having a Baby* (1988)
8. *An Officer and a Gentleman* (1982), *Terms of Endearment* (1983)
9. *Witness* (1985), *Top Gun* (1986)
10. *The Breakfast Club* (1985), *Pretty in Pink* (1986)
11. *Raggedy Man* (1981), *Crimes of the Heart* (1986)
12. *Zelig* (1983), *Hannah and Her Sisters* (1986)
13. *The Elephant Man* (1980), *84 Charing Cross Road* (1987)
14. *White Nights* (1985), *The Mosquito Coast* (1986)

15. *The Witches of Eastwick* (1987), *Moonstruck* (1987)

16. *Jagged Edge* (1985), *Fatal Attraction* (1987)

17. *Scarface* (1983), *The Witches of Eastwick* (1987)

18. *A Room with a View* (1985), *The Lonely Passion of Judith Hearne* (1987)

19. *Trading Places* (1983), *A Fish Called Wanda* (1988)

20. *The Man with Two Brains* (1983), *Peggy Sue Got Married* (1986)

21. *The Fly* (1986), *Beetlejuice* (1988)

22. *The French Lieutenant's Woman* (1981), *Plenty* (1985)

23. *The Postman Always Rings Twice* (1981), Tootsie (1982)

24. *The Colour Purple* (1985), *Jumpin' Jack Flash* (1986)

25. *9½ Weeks* (1986), *My Stepmother Is an Alien* (1988)

26. *Top Gun* (1986), *When Harry Met Sally* (1989)

27. *One from the Heart* (1981), *Paris, Texas* (1984)

28. *Desperately Seeking Susan* (1985), *The Big Blue* (1988)

29. *A Room with a View* (1985), *Maurice* (1987)

30. *Blue Velvet* (1986), *Tough Guys Don't Dance* (1987)

Eighties FASHION

1. Name the fish that featured in an episode of *Fawlty Towers* and was also a hairstyle favoured by pop stars and professional footballers during the eighties.
2. Which trendy eighties watch brand was launched in 1983 by Nicholas G. Hayek, who famously wore several on each arm?
3. What must-have eighties styling tool made hair look like crinkled pasta?
4. Name the lightweight waist-length cotton jacket favoured by skinheads, mod revivalists and scooterboys during the eighties?
5. Which decorative hair accessory was originally called the Scunci, after inventor Rommy Revson's toy poodle?
6. Joan Collins's outfits on the television soap opera *Dynasty* were the epitome of eighties power dressing. What was the name of her character?
7. Which British fashion designer invented the eighties slogan T-shirt?
8. Who popularised fingerless gloves by wearing a pair on the cover of her 1984 album, *Like A Virgin*?

9. Which British singer stuck to her signature look of hoop earrings, a waist-length braid and soft red lipstick?

10. With what garment did ripstop nylon take over the eighties?

11. Who was the first major star to release an exercise video, complete with leg warmers and Lycra?

12. What quintessential eighties hair accessory connected Axl Rose, Olivia Newton-John, John Bon Jovi, Jane Fonda and John McEnroe?

13. Don Johnson in *Miami Vice* was big on pastel suits with rolled up sleeves. What was the name of his detective character?

14. Name the first shoe to feature a 'visible air' window so you could drool over the cushioning technology inside?

15. Designed by Deborah Nadoolman Landis for a 1983 pop video, which iconic jacket sold at auction for $1.8 million on 27th June 2011?

16. Sales of Ray-Ban 3025 Aviator sunglasses rose by 40 per cent after the release of which Tom Cruise film in 1986?

17. During the early eighties, which anarchic fashion designer couple named their shows Savages, Buffalo/Nostalgia of Mud, Punkature, Witches and Worlds End?

18. In the eighties, what power dressing design feature could be seen on Margaret Thatcher, catwalk models and NFL linebackers?

19. How were style icons Sara Dallin, Siobhan Fahey and Keren Woodward better known?

20. What brand of head gear was uniformly worn by individualistic rappers during the eighties without a hint of irony?

1. In the 1984 season, who beat his teammate Alain Prost to the Formula I title by half a point?
2. In which year did Alex Higgins tearfully beckon to his wife and baby daughter after winning the Snooker World Championship for a second time?
3. Which Argentinean soccer player was sold to Napoli for a record fee of £5 million in 1984?
4. In 1987, who became the only player in NBA history other than Wilt Chamberlain to score 3,000 points in a season?
5. In 1989, what freak hockey injury did Buffalo Sabers goalie Clint Malarchuk narrowly survive?
6. In 1980, the American-Cuban runner Rosie Ruiz was stripped of her winners medal for which international marathon race because she hadn't run the whole course?

7. Who were the favourites for the Five Nations rugby tournament in 1983 but ended up with the Wooden Spoon after failing to win a single game?
8. Which British snooker player won the first of six world championship titles in 1981?
9. In 1988, who beat Gabriela Sabatini at the US Open to claim the only Grand Slam in history completed on three surfaces – grass, clay and hard court?
10. Which Brazilian racing driver won the first of his three Formula One titles in 1988?
11. At Caesars Palace in Las Vegas on 6th April1987, which boxer beat Marvin Hagler by a split decision following a three-year retirement?
12. In July 1980, who famously fell to the grass after defeating John McEnroe in an epic five-setter, to claim his last singles title at Wimbledon?
13. Who was the first man to run 1500 metres in under 3 minutes and 30 seconds?
14. In the 1988 Olympics, which American received stitches to his head after hitting it badly on the diving board, and then went on to win the gold medal?
15. Which British athlete won a gold medal in five consecutive Olympic Games from 1984 to 2000?
16. What historic javelin first did Uwe Hohn of East Germany achieve on 20th July 1984?
17. Which boxer was BBC Sports Personality of the Year in 1985?
18. Name the US basketball legend who signed a $25 million contract with the Los Angeles Lakers in 1981.
19. Which British competitive figure skater became Olympic champion in 1980?
20. In 1981, Bob Champion fought back from a terminal cancer diagnosis to win the Grand National on which horse?

1. 'When routine bites hard and ambitions are low.'
2. 'Pressure pushing down on me.'
3. 'Hey, hey, hey, hey Ohhhhho hhhhhohhhohhhhwooooo. Won't you come see about me?'
4. 'The gold road's sure a long road.'
5. 'Don't, Don't, Don't, Don't, Don't, Don't, Don't: Back, caught you lookin' for the same thing.'
6. 'Once upon a time not so long ago, Tommy used to work on the docks.'
7. 'Do you remember a guy that's been in such an early song?'
8. 'How does it feel to treat me like you do?'
9. 'Now there's a backseat lover that's always undercover.'

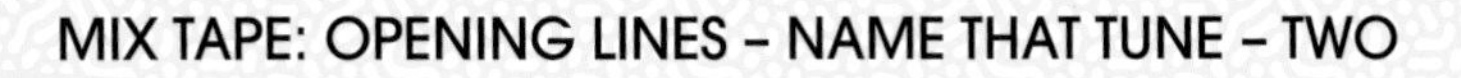

10. 'Who's that gigolo on the street?'

11. 'I am the son and the heir.'

12. 'When you're in love you know you're in love, no matter what you try to do.'

13. 'Under blue moon I saw you so soon you'll take me up in your arms.'

14. 'Welcome to your life, there's no turning back, even while we sleep.'

15. 'Dig if you will the picture of you and I engaged in a kiss.'

16. 'I gotta take a little time, a little time to think things over.'

17. 'Lying in my bed I hear the clock tick and think of you.'

18. 'They told him don't you ever come around here.'

19. 'Travelling in a fried-out Kombi, on a hippie trail, head full of zombie.'

20. 'Long afloat on shipless oceans, I did all my best to smile.'

SITCOMS – TWO

Match the Eighties Sitcom with Its Stars:

After Henry

Bread

Desmond's

Don't Wait Up

Ever Decreasing Circles

Fresh Fields

Home to Roost

In Sickness and in Health

Just Good Friends

Keep it in the Family

May to December

Never the Twain

Only When I Laugh

Shelley

Sorry!

That's My Boy

Three Up, Two Down

Up The Elephant And Round The Castle

Watching

You Rang, M'Lord?

1. Angela Thorne, Michael Elphick, Lysette Anthony, Ray Burdis, John Grillo
2. Paul Shane, Jeffrey Holland, Su Pollard, Donald Hewlett, Michael Knowles
3. Prunella Scales, Joan Sanderson, Janine Wood, Jonathan Newth, Fanny Rowe
4. James Bolam, Peter Bowles, Christopher Strauli, Richard Wilson, Derrick Branche
5. John Thaw, Reece Dinsdale, Elizabeth Bennett, Joan Blackham
6. Donald Sinden, Windsor Davies, Julia Watson, Robin Kermode, Teddy Turner
7. Jean Boht, Peter Howitt, Ronald Forfar, Jonathon Morris, Melanie Hill
8. Paul Bown, Emma Wray, Liza Tarbuck
9. Julia McKenzie, Anton Rodgers, Ann Beach, Fanny Rowe, Debby Cumming
10. Paul Nicholas, Jan Francis, Sylvia Kay, John Ringham, Ann Lynn
11. Ronnie Corbett, Barbara Lott, William Moore, Roy Holder, Marguerite Hardiman
12. Norman Beaton, Carmen Munroe, Ram John Holder, Gyearbuor Asante, Geff Francis
13. Robert Gillespie, Pauline Yates, Stacy Dorning, Sabrina Franklin
14. Anton Rodgers, Eve Matheson, Clive Francis
15. Warren Mitchell, Dandy Nichols, Carmel McSharry
16. Mollie Sugden, Christopher Blake, Jennifer Lonsdale, Harold Goodwin, Clare Richards
17. Richard Briers, Peter Egan, Penelope Wilton, Stanley Lebor, Geraldine Newman
18. Tony Britton, Nigel Havers, Dinah Sheridan, Richard Heffer, Simon Williams
19. Jim Davidson, Brian Hall, John Bardon, Anita Dobson, Sara Corper
20. Hywel Bennett, Belinda Sinclair, Josephine Tewson

1. The long-running British institution, *It's a Knockout* ran until 30th July 1982. In which year did it begin?

2. Which show spawned the Bruce Forsyth catchphrase 'higher or lower'?

3. Which charades-style ITV game show featured Lionel Blair and Una Stubbs as team captains?

4. Name the ITV show that was hosted for its first five years by Nicky Campbell and Carol Smillie.

5. Which gadget-building show ran from 1979 to 1986, hosted by Brian Cant with Professor Heinz Wolff as head judge?

6. In 1984, who succeeded Terry Wogan as the host of *Blankety Blank*?

7. Which ITV show, hosted by Gordon Burns, contained an assault course as well as studio-based intelligence and general knowledge rounds?

8. While Anneka Rice tore breath-

lessly around the countryside in a helicopter finding clues in Channel 4's *Treasure Hunt*, which former newsreader sedately assisted contestants in the studio?

9. In 1984, an unscreened pilot of *Blind Date* (called *It's a Hoot*) was made for London Weekend Television, hosted by camp comedian Duncan Norvelle. What was his coquettish catchphrase?

10. Former ventriloquist and BBC interviewer Derek Batey is best known for hosting the original 450-episode run of which couples show?

11. Which host instructed his guests: 'Keep out of the black, and in the red; there's nothing in this game for two in a bed'?

12. In which show did Jimmy Tarbuck flaunt a briefcase containing the top prize of £1,000 in £1 notes?

13. In 2008, *Going for Gold* was briefly revived for Channel 5, hosted by John Suchet. Who was the original host during the eighties?

14. True or false: the host of *Blockbusters*, Bob Holness, played the saxophone riff on Gerry Rafferty's 1978 hit 'Baker Street'.

15. On *The Price is Right*, contestants had to estimate the price of groceries. Who hosted the show for the first five years?

16. What doubled as the mascot and booby prize of *3-2-1*?

17. On 2nd November 1982, which game show was the first programme to be broadcast on the new British television channel, Channel 4?

18. In 1983, which comedian did Max Bygraves succeed as host of *Family Fortunes*?

19. Who succeeded Bruce Forsyth as host for the last four years of the original run of *The Generation Game*?

20. Name the show hosted by Paul Daniels that ran on BBC1 for nine series from 8th February 1986, in which three married couples competed to win units of time.

Sport

Three

1. Which Olympic event that took place on 24th September 1988 is the subject of Richard Moore's book, *The Dirtiest Race in History*?

2. On 27th June 1988, which unbeaten champion did Mike Tyson destroy in 91 seconds to claim the title of undisputed heavyweight champion of the world?

3. Who won the gold medal in the javelin for Great Britain in the 1984 Summer Olympics?

4. Which famous sporting controversy kicked off at the Azteca Stadium in Mexico City on 22nd June 1986?

5. At Twickenham, in which year did the England rugby team beat the All Blacks at home for the first time since 1936?

6. In 1986, whose nose famously got in the way of a ferocious delivery by West Indies fast bowler Malcolm Marshall?

7. Which British motor racing legend made his Formula 1 debut in Austria in 1980?

8. In 1984, who became the first cricketer to achieve the double triple of 3,000 runs and 300 wickets?

9. Which British football team was relegated in 1987, just five years after becoming European champions?

10. Who caused controversy at the 1984 Olympic Games by wearing a T-Shirt that read: 'Is the world's 2nd greatest athlete gay?'

11. On 11th January 1982, which snooker player achieved the first televised 147 break?

12. Name the 17-year-old who made his Arsenal debut against Sunderland in November 1983 with his shorts on back to front?

13. Who won the Wimbledon Ladies' Singles Championship six times in a row between 1982 and 1987 and again in 1990?

14. In which year did Eddie 'the Eagle' Edwards make his Olympic debut?

15. In 1984, who equalled Jesse Owens' record by winning four gold medals in a single Olympics?

16. Which underdogs humbled Manchester City in a third round FA cup match in 1980?

17. Which Derby-winning Irish racehorse was stolen by masked gunmen on 8th February 1983?

18. An outburst by Tom Gullikson's opponent during a first round match at Wimbledon in 1981 became one of the most famous sound bites in sporting history. What was the four-word phrase?

19. Fatima Whitbread won bronze at the 1984 Olympics and silver in 1988 for which event?

20. Nicknamed 'The Jarrow Arrow', who won the silver medal for the Men's 1500m at the 1984 Summer Olympics?

Eighties SOAP OPERAS

1. Which lunchtime soap opera first aired in 1980 and starred Eileen McCallum throughout the show's lifetime, until it went off air in 2003?
2. Which medical soap opera aired for the last time in 1980?
3. Which Australian soap opera aired in the UK and followed the fate of one family through the Second World War?
4. Which Australian soap opera was set in a fictional hospital in Sydney, Australia?
5. Which Australian soap opera revolved around the lives and loves of the wealthy Hamilton family from Sydney and the Palmers, a working-class family from Melbourne?
6. Which Australian soap opera was set in a small medical practice in rural New South Wales?

7. Which British soap first aired in November 1982, with an episode in which the Collins family moved into a new house and immediately fell out with their neighbours, the Grants?

8. Which soap first aired in Australia in 1985 and has since become the longest-running soap in Australia?

9. Which British soap first aired in 1985 with an episode entitled, 'Murder in Albert Square'?

10. Which long-running British soap opera opened the decade with a storyline in which Rita Fairclough walked out on her husband, Len?

11. Which British soap opera was set on board a passenger ferry in the North Sea?

12. By the 1980s, the cast of which long-running soap opera included Jean Rogers, Shelia Mercier, Toke Townley, Frazier Hines and Frederick Pyne?

13. Which British medical soap opera was into its sixth season by 1980?

14. Which short-lived British soap opera was set in a Salford market?

15. Which police soap opera kicked off with a storyline involving PC Carver and PC Edwards trying to catch a car thief?

16. By the 1980s, the cast of which long-running British soap opera included Jane Rossington, Ann George, Noele Gordon, Edward Clayton and Jack Haig?

17. Which British lunchtime soap opera ran from 1985 to 1988 and was set in a fashion design business?

18. Which soap first aired in 1985 and followed the fortunes of a wealthy yachting community on England's south coast?

19. Which long-running British medical soap first aired in 1986 and starred Derek Thompson, Julia Watson, Brenda Fricker and Bernard Gallagher?

20. In 1980, an episode of which US soap opera achieved the second-highest television viewing audience of a prime time show to date?

FADS AND CRAZES

1. Which best-selling arcade game featured four enemy ghosts called Blinky, Pinky, Inky and Clyde roaming a maze?

2. Which eighties headgear fad was introduced by American entrepreneur, Stephen Askin after he saw John Belushi dressed as a Killer Bee on an episode of *Saturday Night Live*?

3. If your prize possession was a toy containing the signature 'Xavier Roberts', what were you the proud owner of?

4. In 1980, Sony marketed the world's first low-cost portable stereo as the 'Stowaway' in the UK and the 'Soundabout' in the US. By what name was it more popularly known?

5. Annoying and sanctimonious signs to encourage safe driving first appeared in the rear window of cars in the UK in autumn 1984. What did they say?

6. Which thirst-quenching object of desire encouraged us to 'get busy with the fizzy'?

7. In the original Trivial Pursuit board game, what subject area did the colour yellow denote?

8. In the run up to Christmas in 1983, American toy manufacturer Hasbro had 25 factories in Tokyo making a single range of robot action figures. What were they called?

9. One abrasive sensory fad of the eighties used a high-tech process called micro-encapsulation. By what name was it more popularly known?

10. Which series of games developed by Nintendo featured a gorilla and anthropomorphic crocodilians called Kremlings?

11. What was the name of the 'must have' children's bicycle of the early eighties, manufactured by a Nottingham-based company founded in 1885?

12. This leather-bound pocket-sized organiser was registered as a trademark way back on 27th November 1930. Fifty years later it became the must-have status symbol for City yuppies. What was it called?

13. What was the name of the series of 60 Nintendo handheld LCD games that predated the launch of the Game Boy in 1989?

14. Nothing sums up the eighties more vividly than tight-fitting neon garments made out of a polyester-polyurethane copolymer textile. How was it more commonly known?

15. Name the novelty flexible plastic sheets that could be cut, coloured in and then baked to a smaller size in the oven?

16. Name the spherical memory toy with four large coloured buttons that lit up in sequence and then had to be copied.

17. What 3-D puzzle – devised by a Hungarian professor of architecture called Ernö – has sold more than 350 million worldwide since it hit the shelves in 1980?

18. The game cartridge that came bundled with the Atari 2600 Video Computer System boasted 27 games in one, featuring either a tank, biplane or jet. What was it called?

19. A breaded garlic and herb basted chicken cutlet was briefly the height of sophistication during the early part of the decade. First dreamed up by French chefs in pre-revolutionary Russia, what do we call it?

20. The Casio CFX-400 was introduced in 1985. No one really needed one but everybody wanted to wear one. What was it?

Eighties Idols

PRINCE

1. What was Prince's birth name?
2. What neurological condition did Prince suffer from as a child?
3. What was his childhood nickname?
4. He wrote his first song when he was seven. What was it called?
5. What was the name of his third studio album, which was released on 8th October 1980?
6. Who produced, arranged and composed the album?
7. What was the name of the record label that Prince started in 1985?
8. To which faith did Prince belong?
9. What was the name of his backup band?
10. How tall was he?
11. In 1984, what chart feat did Prince accomplish that no one except The Beatles had achieved before?

Name the 1984 American rock musical drama directed by Albert Magnoli in which Prince made his film debut?

Name the song written by Prince that became famous when Sinead O`Connor covered it.

Which Prince song was the top selling single in the US in 1984?

Prince played electric guitar on three songs on which 1989 Madonna album?

What was the name of his female alter ego?

Which of these is not a Prince song: `Raspberry Beret', `Cream', `Pink Cashmere', `Lemon Sorbet'?

The title of his fifth studio album was which number?

Which album was originally planned for release on 7th December 1987, but was delayed until 1994?

During the early nineties, why did Prince become associated with the acronym TAFKAP?

FAMOUS TV Catchphrases

Which TV Programmes are Associated with These Phrases?

1. 'Beedie Beedie Beedie.'
2. 'It's all done in the best possible taste!'
3. 'Our survey says.'
4. 'Smeg head.'
5. 'You plonker.'
6. 'Gizza' job!'
7. 'It's a bummer.'

8. 'Norm!'
9. 'Listen very carefully I shall say this only once.'
10. 'Good grief!'
11. 'Language, Timothy.'
12. 'I have a cunning plan.'
13. 'Can I have a P please, Bob.'
14. 'I ain't goin' on no damn plane, FOOL!'
15. 'Hands up who likes me?'
16. 'This time next year we'll be millionaires.'
17. 'Hello campers.'
18. 'Eep!'
19. 'Look at what you could've won.'
20. 'Goodnight, thank you, and may your god go with you.'

1. Who made her final appearance after 20 years on the show in April 1980?
2. Which long-running character was born to Gail and Brian in an episode that aired on New Year's Eve, 1980?
3. Whose was the wedding of the year in July 1981?

4. Which character had an extra-marital affair with Mike Baldwin in February 1983?

5. Who was killed off in a car crash in December 1983?

6. Who left the Street in 1984 to live in Portugal?

7. Which character died in hospital in November 1984?

8. Who became Hilda Ogden's lodger at No.13 in May 1985?

9. Who did Ken Barlow thump in January 1986, with the line, 'I've had enough of your poison in my family'?

10. What was Hilda Ogden left in her friend Ada Arrowsmith's will in April 1986?

11. What small business was opened on the Street in April 1986 by Audrey Roberts?

12. Whose was the wedding of the year in May 1986?

13. After Jack Duckworth secretly entered himself in a competition for 'Husband of the Year' in his wife's name in May 1986, what prize did Vera collect?

14. Who got trapped at The Rover's Return in June 1986 after a fuse box exploded?

15. When Gail Tilsley revealed that she was pregnant in July 1986, which two men were the potential fathers?

16. Who did Bet Lynch marry in September 1987?

17. A reported 26.8 million viewers tuned in on Christmas Day, 1987 to see which much-loved character leave the show?

18. Whose was the wedding of the year in November 1988?

19. Which character famously remarked in 1989, while smiling through marital problems, 'It's not a smile, it's a lid on a scream'?

20. Which character was hit by a Blackpool tram while chasing Rita Fairclough in December 1989?

One Hit WONDERS

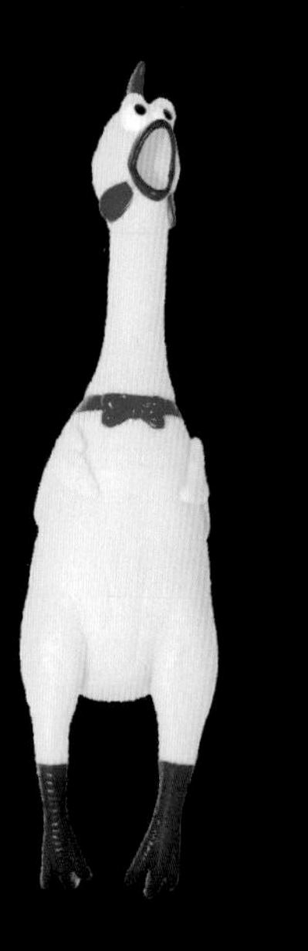

1. Who topped the UK charts in March 1980 with the song, 'Together We Are Beautiful'?
2. Robert Altman was paid $70,000 to direct the film *M*A*S*H* but his fourteen-year-old son earned more than $1 million by co-writing its theme tune. What was the title?
3. Which Stockport primary school choir hit No.1 in December 1980 with 'There's No One Quite Like Grandma'?
4. Which Joe Dolce novelty song kept Ultravox's 'Vienna' off the top spot?
5. Name the American R&B singer who topped the UK charts in June 1982 with her only Top 40 hit.

6. In October 1987, alternative rock band A.R. Kane and electronica group Colourbox briefly paired up as MARRS to create which house music blockbuster?
7. Which 1988 Robin Beck hit was originally recorded for a Coca-Cola advert?
8. 'Xanadu' was a hit in 1980 for Olivia Newton-John and which British rock group from Birmingham?
9. Who paired up with Mick Jagger for the 1985 hit, 'Dancing in the Street'?
10. The 1985 Barbara Dixon and Elaine Page hit, 'I Know Him so Well' appeared in which theatrical musical?
11. The 1987 hit 'I Knew You Were Waiting For Me' paired George Michael and which American singing legend?
12. Who teamed up for the 1982 chart topper, 'Ebony and Ivory'?
13. Queen and David Bowie scored a hit in 1981 with which song?
14. In 1986, which comic quartet helped Cliff Richard reach No.1 again?
15. American club DJ and house music pioneer, Steve 'Silk' Hurley, had a massive solo hit in 1987 with which landmark house anthem?
16. In 1988, The KLF reached No.1 with their electronic novelty mash up song, 'Doctorin' the Tardis' using which sci-fi pseudonym?
17. Which 1989 hit briefly united The Christians, Paul McCartney, Holly Johnson, Gerry Marsden and Stock Aitken Waterman?
18. Name the Black Lace style parody that put Spitting Image at No.1 for three weeks in 1986.
19. Roland Rat reached No.32 in 1983 with a cover of which Elvis Presley song?
20. In January 1983, Orville reached No.4 and sold more than 400,000 copies singing about his wish. What was it?

1. Name the eighties host of *Call My Bluff* who was satirised in *Private Eye* as 'Smuggins'.

2. Which BBC radio comedy panel game was hosted by Humphrey Lyttelton from 1972 until his death in 2008?

3. Which quiz show began with the ominous theme tune 'Approaching Menace' by the British composer Neil Richardson?

4. Which writer, politician and chef was a regular on the BBC radio comedy panel game *Just a Minute* from 1967 to 2009, making him its longest-serving guest?

5. Whose petulant tantrums on the show were often prefaced by the catchphrase, 'I've come all the way from Great Portland Street'?

6. Which BBC topical radio panel game currently hosted by Miles Jupp, was hosted during the early eighties by Simon Hoggart?

7. Frank Muir was one regular team captain of *Call My Bluff* during the eighties; which humour author and magazine columnist was the other?

8. Which BBC1 music quiz programme originally aired from 4th July 1981 to 28th December 1984, hosted by Mike Read?

9. On which long-running quiz show was former England rugby player Bill Beaumont a team captain?

10. Name the show that first aired on ITV on 3rd April 1987, in which David Frost snooped around the houses of mystery celebrities.

11. Which show featured a golden robot called Mr Chips?

12. Which former presenter of *Blue Peter* hosted the adult version of *Connections* on ITV in which contestants had to answer general knowledge questions to guess the connections between nine pictures?

13. *Chain Letters* was first broadcast on 7th September 1987 on ITV. Who was its original host?

14. On which long-running general knowledge television quiz could you hear instructions such as: 'father and elder child only'?

15. In which show, originally presented by Tom O'Connor, did contestants attempt to identify a song after bidding down to hear the fewest notes?

16. Name the London taxi driver who hit the headlines after winning *Mastermind* in 1980.

17. What is the name of the fictional silent scorer on *I'm Sorry I Haven't a Clue*?

18. Which general knowledge quiz show originally ran from 11th January 1988 to 19th December 2003 on Channel 4, presented by William G. Stewart?

19. At the time of his death in June 2005, which panel show host had made more than 10,000 appearances and clocked up more hours than anyone else on British television?

20. What succinct advice did Northern Irish comedian Roy Walker frequently give to contestants on *Catchphrase*?

THE ROYAL Wedding

1. The Wedding of Prince Charles and Diana Spencer took place on in in 29th July which year?
2. Where did they get married: St Paul's Cathedral or Westminster Abbey?
3. How old was Diana on her wedding day: 19, 20 or 23?
4. How old was Charles: 32, 36 or 39?
5. All of Europe's crowned heads attended, with the exception of one. Who stayed away because of the newlyweds' planned visit to Gibraltar?
6. How many people officially attended the wedding ceremony: 2,500, 3,500, 4,500?
7. Which couple designed Diana's gown?
8. 10,000 what were hand-sewn into the gown?
9. How long was Diana's train: 7.6 m, 12.5 m or 21.5 m?

10. Who led the traditional Church of England service?

11. Diana fluffed her wedding vows. How did she incorrectly refer to the prince: 'Charles Philip Arthur George', 'Charles Arthur Philip George' or 'Philip Charles Arthur George'?

12. What mistake did Charles make during his vows?

13. Did Diana promise to obey Charles?

14. What Elgar composition accompanied them as they walked back down the aisle together?

15. Who was the official photographer at the wedding?

16. After the ceremony, how many guests joined the couple at Buckingham Palace for the wedding breakfast: 120, 650 or 1,250?

17. How many wedding cakes were used at the wedding breakfast: 1, 2 or 27?

18. What was held at White's, a 300-year old gentleman's club in London?

19. How much did Prince Charles and Diana's wedding cost British taxpayers: £5 million, £10 million or £30 million?

20. In which year did they divorce?

Science Fiction on TELEVISION

1. The American crime-busting television series *Knight Rider* had a space age artificially intelligent Pontiac Firebird Trans Am car called KITT. What did the acronym stand for?
2. *Mork and Mindy* was a spin-off from which American television sitcom?
3. What Orcan profanity did Mork frequently use?
4. What was the name of the world's first computer-generated TV host, played by Matt Frewer in elaborate prosthetic make up?
5. What was the name of the small silver robot in the American science-fiction adventure television series, *Buck Rogers in the 25th Century*?
6. What was the name of the sentient disc-shaped computer that he carried on his chest?
7. What was the first name of the lead female character played by Erin Gray?
8. What was the name of the spaceship that featured in the first three seasons of *Blake's 7*?

9. What was the name of the highly advanced but short-tempered supercomputer housed in a large transparent Perspex box that featured from the end of the first series?

10. What kind of spaceship was the eponymous *Red Dwarf* in the sci-fi sitcom that debuted on BBC2 on 15th February 1988?

11. Which laconic stand-up comedian originally voiced the senile computer, Holly?

12. Name the neurotic robotic servant who was rescued from the crashed spaceship *Nova 5* in the second series?

13. At the end of the eighteenth series of *Doctor Who*, broadcast on 21st March 1981, Tom Baker as the Fourth Doctor regenerated into a new, younger body – the Fifth Doctor, played by which actor?

14. Which actor, who appeared in the 1987 cult film *Withnail and I*, was the producer's first choice for the Fifth Doctor, but was unavailable?

15. Which actor, who appeared in the 1987 cult film *Withnail and I*, played the Eighth Doctor?

16. Who played the character Zaphod Beeblebrox in the BBC television adaptation of Douglas Adams's *The Hitchhiker's Guide to the Galaxy*?

17. Born Sandra Searles, the American-British actress played the brilliant mathematician and astrophysicist Trillian? What was her acting name?

18. Name the 1981 BBC six-episode adaptation of the novel by John Wyndham, which starred John Duttine as farmer Bill Masen?

19. Which British television science-fiction series starred David McCallum and Joanna Lumley?

20. What was the name of the unpopular law enforcement science-fiction series that was canned after just nine episodes in 1987?

LIVE AID

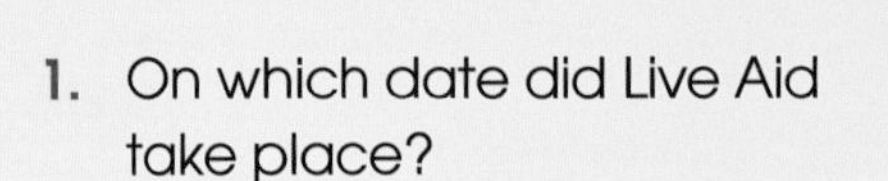

1. On which date did Live Aid take place?
2. Who were the two main organising front men?
3. Which American actor hosted the JFK concert?
4. Which band opened the concert at Wembley?
5. What song did Queen sing first?
6. Who sang 'The Note Heard Round the World'?
7. Who had part of her dress ripped away by Mick Jagger?
8. Which group briefly reformed for the first time in three years to perform at Wembley?

9. Who performed live at both Wembley Stadium and JFK?

10. How did this performer cross the Atlantic Ocean?

11. Which UK TV personality piloted the helicopter that took the performer to Heathrow Airport?

12. Who announced to the JFK crowd, 'this is your Woodstock, and it's long overdue' before leading them in singing 'Amazing Grace'?

13. U2 spent 14 minutes performing which song from their 1984 album, *The Unforgettable Fire*?

14. Why did viewers in America miss several songs?

15. Which band, with technical difficulties and Phil Collins standing in on drums, suffered 'one of the worst rock and roll reunions of all time' at Live Aid?

16. Whose microphone failed for the first two minutes of his performance of 'Let it Be'?

17. Which song by The Beatles did Elvis Costello sing after asking the audience to help him 'sing this old northern English folk song'?

18. When Bob Dylan broke a guitar string, who gave him his own and then shrugged and played air guitar?

19. Which BBC Live Aid presenter criticised the event organisers for failing to include a single African performer on the bill?

20. At the end of the Wembley concert, which two stars lifted Bob Geldof onto their shoulders?

Name the ACTOR

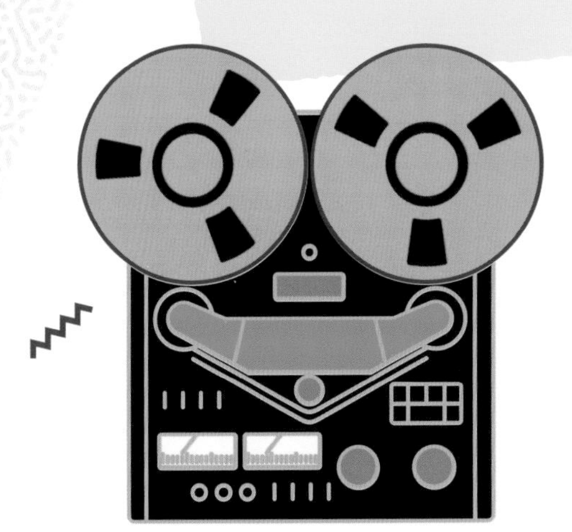

Name the Actor in Both Films

1. *Any Which Way You Can* (1980), *Sudden Impact* (1983)
2. *The Golden Child* (1986), *Coming to America* (1988)
3. *Highlander* (1986), *Indiana Jones and the Last Crusade* (1989)
4. *Breathless* (1983), *Pretty Woman* (1990)
5. *Teen Wolf* (1985), *Bright Lights, Big City* (1988)

6. *Peggy Sue Got Married* (1986), *Moonstruck* (1987)
7. *The Untouchables* (1987), *Field of Dreams* (1989)
8. *A View to a Kill* (1985), *Communion* (1989)
9. *Pretty in Pink* (1986), *Sex, Lies, and Videotape* (1989)
10. *Scarface* (1983), *Sea of Love* (1989)
11. *Risky Business* (1983), *Rain Man* (1988)
12. *The Breakfast Club* (1985), *Young Guns* (1988)
13. *Red Sonja* (1985), *Red Heat* (1988)
14. *Splash* (1984) *The Money Pit* (1986)
15. *Blade Runner* (1982), *Witness* (1985)
16. *Rumble Fish* (1983), *Angel Heart* (1987)
17. *Ferris Bueller's Day Off* (1986), *Torch Song Trilogy* (1988)
18. *Ishtar* (1987), *Rain Man* (1988)
19. *The King of Comedy* (1982), *The Mission* (1986)
20. *Rocky III* (1982), *First Blood* (1982)
21. *Die Hard* (1988), *Look Who's Talking* (1989)
22. *Cocoon* (1985), *Short Circuit* (1986)
23. *Romancing the Stone* (1984), *The War of the Roses* (1989)
24. *The Killing Fields* (1984), *Dangerous Liaisons* (1988)
25. *A Room with a View* (1985), *The Unbearable Lightness of Being* (1988)
26. *Platoon* (1986), *The Last Temptation of Christ* (1988)
27. *The Lost Boys* (1987), *Young Guns* (1988)
28. *A Few Good Men* (1992), *The Witches of Eastwick* (1987)
29. *The World According to Garp* (1982), *The Adventures of Baron Munchausen* (1988)
30. *Tootsie* (1982), *Scrooged* (1988)

ALTERNATIVE Comedy

1. Which fat Liverpudlian Marxist was the first MC of London's Comedy Store?
2. Who founded The Comic Strip troupe and directed most of its films?
3. Name the spoof heavy metal band that was created for the first series of *The Comic Strip Presents ...*
4. Name the anarchic stage duo formed by Rik Mayall and Ade Edmondson.
5. Which 1983–1984 television series starred Ben Elton, Stephen Fry, Hugh Laurie, Emma Thompson, Siobhan Redmond and Paul Shearer?
6. Where did Dawn French and Jennifer Saunders meet?
7. Who created the spoof actor character Nicholas Craig?
8. What was the name of Vyvyan's hamster in *The Young Ones*?
9. Which co-creator of *The Young Ones* is the third cousin of singer Olivia Newton-John?

10. What was the follow up to *Five Go Mad in Dorset* in the second series of *The Comic Strip Presents...*?

11. Who was Jerzei Balowski?

12. Who played Mike-The-Cool-Person in *The Young Ones*?

13. Name the flat share comedy that starred Dawn French, Jennifer Saunders, Tracy Ullman and Ruby Wax?

14. Which Comic Strip actor found international fame in the *Harry Potter* films?

15. What was the name of Rik Mayall's West Midlands solo character?

16. Who was known on the comedy circuit during the early part of her career as 'The Sea Monster'?

17. What was the name of the first feature-length *Comic Strip* film?

18. Name the father-son comedy music duo formed by Simon Brint and Rowland Rivron.

19. Which Comedy Store breakthrough act played Pepi the Poisoner in the 1992 film *Carry on Columbus*?

20. What was the name of Harry Enfield's Greek kebab shop-owner character from *Friday Night Live*?

Advertising

Two

1. Drinking which brand of lager allowed a Sloane Ranger to deliver in perfect Cockney the phrase: 'The water in Majorca don't taste like what it oughta'?
2. What was 'the biggest snack pennies can buy'?
3. What was 'too orangey for crows'?
4. Upon the advice of football player Ian Rush, what did a young lad drink so that one day he might be good enough to play for Accrington Stanley?

5. What drink had a 'totally tropical taste'?

6. Which chocolate biscuit was advertised by overdubbing footage from *The Wizard of Oz*?

7. 'No three things are quite as good together as . . . ' a what?

8. Which shampoo was 'so mild, you can wash your hair as often as you wish'?

9. Which product had an advert which ended with the line '. . . and Michael, Remember Preston'?

10. According to the adverts, what did the hot oat cereal Ready Brek make children do?

11. What was the 'longer lasting snack'?

12. What was a sign of good taste at an Ambassador's party?

13. Which breakfast cereal was advertised by the British middle distance runner Steve Cram?

14. Which brand of lager was advertised by animated cartoon Vikings?

15. Complete the slogan: 'Thank _______ it's Friday! '

16. Which spreadable blend of vegetable oils and butter was advertised by Willie Rushton?

17. Which thick creamy condiment was advertised by the comedy entertainer Bob Carolgees?

18. What product offered: 'pure tasting sweetness, but not one single calorie'?

19. What 'brings your taste buds back to life again'?

20. Which weight-conscious food product introduced 'The Pinch'

The King of Pop

MICHAEL JACKSON

1. Where was he born?
2. What was his middle name?
3. What injury did he sustain during the production of a 1984 Pepsi advertisement?
4. Name his 1982 best-selling album of all time, with an estimated 45 million copies sold worldwide.
5. What did he pay $47 million for in 1985 and sold a share of to Sony ten years later for $95 million?
6. Which British football team did Michael Jackson support?
7. How many Grammys did he win in 1984: 4, 6 or 8?
8. With whom did he co-write the 1985 charity single 'We Are the World'?
9. Who was his favourite animated character?

10. Why did he wear a black armband?

11. How many times was he inducted into the Rock and Roll Hall of Fame?

12. He once admitted to Daryl Hall that he lifted the bass line of 'Billie Jean' from which Hall & Oates song?

13. Which Academy Award-winning American filmmaker directed the video for Michael Jackson's 1987 hit, 'Bad'?

14. What first did the video for Billie Jean achieve?

15. What was the name of the autobiography he released in 1988?

16. To which legendary Hollywood dancer did he dedicate the book?

17. What was the name of his pet chimpanzee?

18. He once owned a pet called 'Muscles'. What kind of animal was it?

19. How much did he pay in 1988 for the 2,700 acres of land on which he built his Neverland Ranch: \$5 million, \$17 million or \$27 million?

20. What was the name of the skin disease from which he claimed he suffered?

Characters in the Eighties

EASTENDERS

1. Which character appeared in the series from episode one for five years, was addicted to gambling and had his wife sectioned?
2. Which troubled character funded a drug addiction with blackmail and prostitution before choking to death on her own vomit in 1989?
3. Which East End barrow boy was in a gay relationship with yuppie Colin Russell from 1986 to 1989?
4. Which archetypal East End matriarch was played by Anna Wing until the character was killed off in July 1988?
5. Who was the pub landlady with the stormy marriage, the penchant for drink and the

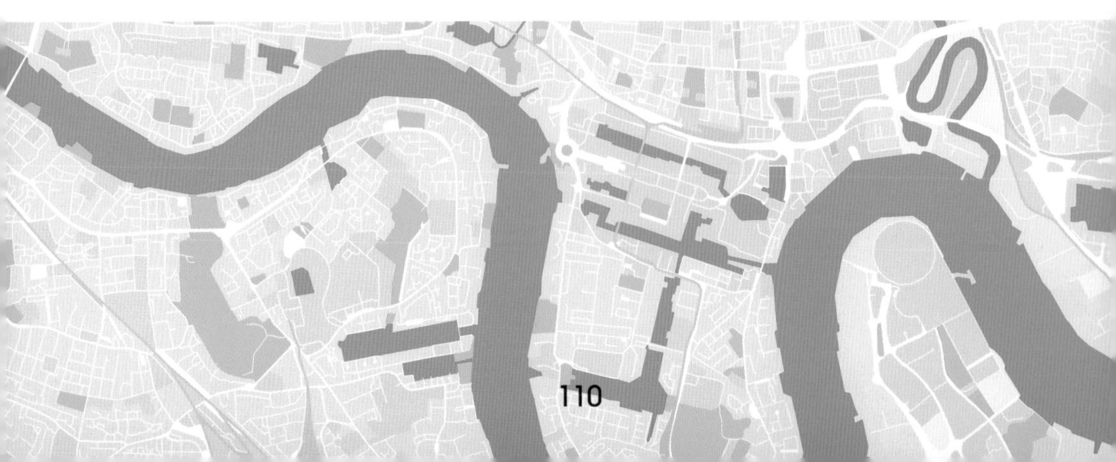

adopted daughter, whose final marital breakdown was watched by 30.1 million viewers on Christmas Day 1986?

6. Which meek and mild character was played by Tom Watt from 1985 until 1988?

7. Which character was Pauline Fowler's niece, and appeared in the show for the first time in 1988?

8. Who was the curate at the local church who comforted a troubled Sharon Watts from his first appearance in October 1987?

9. Who was the pub landlord everyone loved to hate?

10. Which allotment-loving character would ultimately suffer mental illness, prison and a brain haemorrhage?

11. Which character was played by Gretchin Franklin?

12. Who was Ethel's constant companion?

13. Who was the show's second-longest running character, appearing from the first episode in 1985 until Christmas day, 2006?

14. Who was found by Arthur Fowler, Den Watts and Ali Osman in the very first episode, half-dead after having been brutally attacked in his flat?

15. Which recurring villain made his first appearance in the very first episode, written in by the creators as an after-thought, with a character outline which read, 'His image is exclusively macho. Vanishes for weeks on end. His Mum doesn't ask questions'?

16. Whose character unravelled tragically after discovering her son Hassan had suffered cot death in 1985?

17. What was the name of Sharon Watts' Standard Poodle?

18. Which 16-year-old character fell pregnant after an affair with her best mate's father?

19. Who ran the laundrette with Pauline Fowler?

20. Which character was the show's first pin-up?

Blackadder

1. Which year was the first episode of *Blackadder* shown on British television: 1981, 1982, 1983 or 1984?
2. What was Blackadder's first name?
3. Who played Blackadder's father, Richard IV in the first series?
4. Which castle in Northumberland was used for location shots?
5. Which pair of writers devised the idea for the sitcom while working on *Not the Nine O'Clock News*?
6. Who was brought in to replace one of them before the second series?
7. What was Baldrick's catchphrase?
8. Which one of these actors did not appear in any of the *Blackadder* episodes: Peter Cook, Tom Baker, Helen Atkinson-Wood, Frank Finlay, Jennifer Saunders, Patsy Byrne, Nigel Planer, Ben Elton?

9. In the unscreened pilot, which character was played by Philip Fox?
10. Who played Prince George?
11. Which recurring character had the catchphrase 'Baaaaah'?
12. Which pie shop owner was often mentioned but never seen in *Blackadder II*?
13. Who played Queen Elizabeth I in the second series?
14. Who appeared briefly as 'Mad Gerald' in the final episode of the first series?
15. What two things, 'must thee know of the Wisewoman'?
16. In *Blackadder Goes Forth*, what name did Baldrick carve on a bullet?
17. In the second episode of *Blackadder Goes Forth*, two characters in the firing squad were called 'Fraser' and 'Jones' in homage to which other British sitcom?
18. What recurring role did Rik Mayall play?
19. In *Blackadder Goes Forth*, why did Blackadder stick a pencil up each nostril and wear underpants on his head?
20. Producer John Lloyd has claimed that during the early nineties, half the regimental goats in the British armed forces were named after which *Blackadder* character?

Answers

The Year That Was - 1980

1. The New Israeli Sheqel
2. Audi Quattro
3. Zimbabwe
4. Rock festival
5. Iran
6. Brian McFadden
7. Kramer vs. Kramer
8. Iranian Embassy
9. Mount St. Helens
10. Cable News Network (CNN)
11. Pope John Paul II
12. Iran
13. Lech Wałęsa
14. Switzerland
15. lady's, turning
16. James Callaghan
17. The Maze Prison
18. John Lennon
19. Colonel Harland David Sanders
20. Japan

The Year That Was - 1981

1. Yellow
2. Bobby Sands
3. Augusto Pinochet
4. London Marathon
5. Jodie Foster
6. 'Making Your Mind Up'
7. Brixton
8. Bob Marley
9. Pope John Paul II
10. François Mitterrand
11. Peter Sutcliffe
12. Library
13. It was the only time in twentieth century Test cricket history that a side won after following on.
14. Wedding of Charles, Prince of Wales, and Lady Diana Spencer
15. 24-hour video music channel
16. Only Fools and Horses
17. Simon & Garfunkel
18. Anwar Sadat
19. Admitting women to holy orders
20. Muhammad Ali

The Year That Was - 1982

1. Mark Thatcher, son of British Prime Minister Margaret Thatcher
2. Unemployment in the United Kingdom
3. The first computer virus
4. The Barbican Centre
5. Chariots of Fire
6. The Falklands War
7. General Belgrano
8. Gilles Villeneuve
9. Aston Villa
10. Northumberland
11. Spain
12. Spain
13. Prince William
14. Roy Jenkins
15. Michael Fagan
16. Compact disc
17. Smiley emoticon
18. Experimental Prototype Community Of Tomorrow
19. Henry VIII
20. Michael Jackson's Thriller

The Year That Was - 1983

1. Hawaii
2. Aldo Moro
3. Seat belts
4. Klaus Barbie
5. Challenger
6. Tokyo
7. The Hitler Diaries
8. Pioneer 10
9. She became the first American woman in space aboard Space Shuttle Challenger
10. Nintendo Entertainment System (NES)
11. Helicopter
12. Kiss
13. HM Maze Prison
14. Roy Hattersley
15. Lockheed
16. The metre
17. Grenada
18. Heathrow Airport
19. The Jules Rimet Trophy (World Cup)
20. The McNugget

The Year That Was – 1984

1. Brunei
2. Nissan
3. The Miners' Strike
4. Marvin Gaye
5. US President Ronald Reagan
6. Tommy Cooper
7. Yvonne Fletcher
8. Sweden
9. Mark Zuckerberg
10. Cirque du Soleil
11. A space walk
12. Los Angeles
13. Discovery
14. Hot air balloon
15. Summit Mount Everest
16. Perform a space walk
17. An IRA bombing
18. Indira Gandhi, Prime Minister of India
19. Famine in Ethiopia
20. Bhopal

The Year That Was – 1985

1. Michel and Albert Roux
2. 15 mph
3. Red telephone boxes
4. Televised debate
5. Clive Ponting
6. EastEnders
7. Millwall
8. New Coke
9. The hole in the ozone layer
10. Juventus
11. Ruth Lawrence
12. Rainbow Warrior
13. London and Philadelphia
14. The wreck of the RMS Titanic
15. PC Keith Blakelock
16. Wayne Rooney
17. Peugeot 309
18. Garry Kasparov
19. The Anglo-Irish Agreement
20. Comic Relief

The Year That Was – 1986

1. Michael Heseltine
2. The Channel Tunnel
3. Today
4. FREDDIE STARR ATE MY HAMSTER
5. Prince Andrew and Sarah Ferguson
6. Out of Africa
7. John McCarthy
8. Chelsea
9. Robert Pattinson
10. Pingu
11. British Leyland
12. Gary Lineker
13. Nissan
14. The People's Republic of China
15. Neighbours
16. M25 London Orbital Motorway
17. AIDS
18. Guinness
19. British Gas
20. Sending his innocent fiancée on an El Al flight from Heathrow airport, carrying a bomb

---

The Year That Was – 1987

1. Aretha Franklin
2. Prince Edward
3. Terry Waite
4. Edwina Currie
5. MS Herald of Free Enterprise
6. The Simpsons
7. Andy Murray
8. Rugby World Cup game
9. Near Red Square
10. Five
11. Docklands Light Railway
12. Hungerford
13. A Momentary Lapse of Reason
14. IKEA
15. 15 million
16. Black Monday
17. Ejected from the plane, which continued unpiloted until it ran out of fuel and crashed into the Irish Sea
18. Lester Piggott
19. King's Cross
20. Windows 2.0

Answers

The Year That Was - 1988

1. Peugeot 405
2. Red Nose Day
3. Pound note
4. £60,000
5. Prince Charles
6. Sandy Lyle
7. Kenneth Williams
8. Nurses
9. Celine Dion
10. Adele
11. Wimbledon FC
12. Hello!
13. Nelson Mandela
14. Damien Hirst
15. Piper Alpha
16. Paul Gascoigne
17. Ian Paisley
18. Harold Wilson
19. She had incorrectly stated that most of Britain's eggs were infected with the salmonella bacteria
20. Yellowstone National Park

The Year That Was - 1989

1. It described him as having become like the character Basil Fawlty
2. Sky Television
3. Salman Rushdie
4. Behind a bunch of daffodils
5. Complete ten years in office
6. Sonia Sutcliffe, wife of 'Yorkshire Ripper' Peter Sutcliffe
7. He stood in front of a tank in Tiananmen Square holding bags of groceries.
8. Laurence Olivier
9. Daniel Radcliffe
10. Electronic tagging
11. Princess Anne and Captain Mark Phillips
12. John Major
13. The Guildford Four
14. The Berlin Wall
15. It was televised live
16. Nigel Martyn
17. Doctor Who
18. A Grand Day Out
19. Downing Street
20. The Ford Escort

Classic Eighties Novels

1. Waterland, Graham Swift
2. Love in the Time of Cholera, Gabriel García Márquez
3. Oranges Are Not the Only Fruit, Jeanette Winterson
4. A Case of Knives, Candia McWilliam
5. Contact, Carl Sagan
6. Schindler's Ark, Thomas Keneally
7. Empire of the Sun, J.G. Ballard
8. The Wasp Factory, Iain Banks
9. Earthly Powers, Anthony Burgess
10. Beloved, Toni Morrison
11. Changes, Danielle Steel
12. Lincoln: A Novel, Gore Vidal
13. The Restaurant at the End of the Universe, Douglas Adams
14. The House of the Spirits, Isabel Allende
15. V for Vendetta, Alan Moore
16. The Silence of the Lambs, Thomas Harris
17. London Fields, Martin Amis
18. The Colour of Magic, Terry Pratchett
19. Hawksmoor, Peter Ackroyd
20. An Indecent Obsession, Colleen McCullough
21. The Sicilian, Mario Puzo
22. Watchmen, Alan Moore
23. Sour Sweet, Timothy Mo
24. The Colour Purple, Alice Walker
25. Small World, David Lodge
26. The Tommyknockers, Stephen King
27. The Fourth Protocol, Frederick Forsyth
28. The Satanic Verses, Salman Rushdie
29. Firestarter, Stephen King
30. The Pillars of the Earth, Ken Follett
31. Clear and Present Danger, Tom Clancy
32. The Unbearable Lightness of Being, Milan Kundera
33. The Russia House, John Le Carré
34. Neuromancer, William Gibson
35. Blow Your House Down, Pat Barker
36. Hotel du Lac, Anita Brookner

Classic Eighties Novels, continued

37. The Alchemist, Paulo Coelho
38. A Confederacy of Dunces, John Kennedy Toole
39. A History of the World in 10½ Chapters, Julian Barnes
40. Hollywood Wives, Jackie Collins
41. The Good Apprentice, Iris Murdoch
42. The Bonfire of the Vanities, Tom Wolfe
43. Perfume: The Story of a Murderer, Patrick Süskind
44. Mistral's Daughter, Judith Krantz
45. A Prayer for Owen Meany, John Irving
46. The Bourne Identity, Robert Ludlum
47. The White Hotel, D.M. Thomas
48. The Remains of the Day, Kazuo Ishiguro
49. The Name of the Rose, Umberto Eco
50. The Handmaid's Tale, Margaret Atwood

Diana, Princess of Wales

1. The Royal Sandringham Estate
2. Three (two older sisters and one younger brother)
3. Eight years old
4. Lady Diana Spencer
5. Twice
6. Diana's 26-year-old sister, Lady Sarah McCorquodale
7. Prince Charles proposed to her and she accepted.
8. Kindergarten teacher
9. British citizen
10. Kensington Palace and Highgrove House
11. Diana's first pregnancy
12. Arthur
13. Camilla Parker-Bowles
14. James Hewitt
15. The Queen
16. Great Ormond Street Hospital for Children
17. Bulimia
18. The Rottweiler
19. That ridiculous creature
20. 5′10 3/4″ (1.79m)

Eighties Television

1. Kristin Shepard
2. Arthur Daley
3. No one. There was no actual character called Juliet Bravo. Stephanie Turner played Inspector Jean Darblay for the first two series and then Anna Carteret was Inspector Kate Longton.
4. Miami Vice
5. Zeus and Apollo
6. The Dukes of Hazzard
7. Diff'rent Strokes
8. Boston
9. Neither cop ever drew his gun
10. The A-Team
11. Beadle's About
12. Moonlighting
13. Brideshead Revisited
14. Lee Majors
15. Jim Bergerac
16. Fame
17. Dempsey and Makepeace
18. Tomorrow's World
19. The Wonder Years
20. Sharon Gless was Christine Cagney; Tyne Daly was Mary Beth Lacey

Advertising - One

1. The Yellow Pages
2. Shake n' Vac
3. American Express credit card
4. Fry's Turkish Delight
5. Cadbury's Flake
6. 'O sole mio'
7. Hamlet Cigars
8. Scotch
9. Carling Black Label
10. Stelios Havatzias (baby)
11. Bran Flakes
12. Birds Eye Steakhouse Grills
13. Apple Macintosh Computer
14. Terry's Chocolate Orange
15. Nick Kamen
16. Levi 501 Jeans
17. Vitalite
18. Findus Crispy Pancakes
19. They're bootiful
20. Kraft Dairylea

Science

1. MS-DOS, which IBM rebranded to PC DOS
2. Saturn
3. The mass extinction of the dinosaurs was caused by a large asteroid impact 66 million years ago.
4. Space Shuttle Columbia
5. The ZX81
6. The Commodore 64
7. Halley's Comet
8. Channel 4
9. The Internet
10. Untethered space walk
11. Apple Computer released the Macintosh personal computer
12. Tetris
13. Bovine spongiform encephalopathy (BSE)
14. Commercial Internet domain name with the suffix .com
15. Windows 1.0
16. Laptop computer
17. DNA fingerprinting
18. Prozac
19. The Channel Tunnel
20. A Brief History of Time

Eighties Idols – Tom Cruise

1. Endless Love
2. Sean Penn
3. Francis Ford Coppola
4. Their virginity
5. 'Old Time Rock and Roll'
6. It rolls down a hill into Lake Michigan
7. American football
8. Lea Thompson
9. The death of his father
10. Ridley Scott
11. Val Kilmer
12. All of them
13. Paul Newman
14. Martin Scorsese
15. Bryan Brown
16. 'Cocktails & Dreams'
17. Charlie Babbitt
18. K-Mart
19. Oliver Stone
20. 3rd July

Mix Tape: Opening Lines – Name That Tune

1. 'I Wanna Dance With Somebody' (Whitney Houston)
2. 'Take On Me' (A-ha)
3. 'What's Love Got to Do with It' (Tina Turner)
4. 'Africa' (Toto)
5. 'Never Gonna Give You Up' (Rick Astley)
6. 'Total Eclipse of the Heart' (Bonnie Tyler)
7. 'Modern Love' (David Bowie)
8. 'This Charming Man' (The Smiths)
9. 'Straight Outta Compton' (N.W.A.)
10. 'Drive' (The Cars)
11. 'Into the Groove' (Madonna)
12. 'Running Up That Hill' (Kate Bush)
13. 'West End Girls' (Pet Shop Boys)
14. 'Come on Eileen' (Dexys Midnight Runners)
15. 'End of the World as We Know It' (R.E.M.)
16. 'The Whole Of The Moon' (The Waterboys)
17. 'With Or Without You' (U2)
18. 'Fairytale Of New York' (The Pogues)
19. 'Once In A Lifetime' (Talking Heads)
20. 'That's Entertainment' (The Jam)

Food and Drink

1. Top Deck
2. Square
3. Golden Wonder
4. Topic
5. Marathon (Snickers)
6. Blue Band
7. 10p
8. FISH 'n' CHIPS
9. Starbar
10. Yorkie Bar
11. Tooty Frooties
12. Gold Nuggets
13. 54321
14. Banjo
15. Cadbury's Caramel
16. Cabana
17. Trio!
18. Secret
19. Wispa
20. HB Funny Feet

Answers

Children's Television

1. Fraggle Rock
2. The Flumps
3. Jigsaw
4. Cheggers Plays Pop
5. Roland Rat
6. Inspector Gadget
7. Susan Tully
8. He-Man and She-Ra
9. Multi-Coloured Swap Shop and Saturday Superstore
10. Yvette Fielding
11. 2020
12. David Jason
13. The Smurfs
14. Press Gang
15. Metal Mickey
16. The Really Wild Show
17. Computer
18. Timmy Mallett
19. Fruit and vegetables
20. Gordon the Gopher

Eighties Idols – Whitney Houston

1. Dionne Warwick
2. Her mother, gospel singer Emily 'Cissy' (Drinkard) Houston
3. 'I'm Every Woman'
4. Seventeen
5. She insisted that Whitney graduate from high school.
6. Arista
7. Teddy Pendergrass
8. Whitney Houston
9. 'You Give Good Love'
10. 'Saving All My Love For You'
11. 1986
12. 'How Will I Know'
13. MTV
14. George Benson
15. 'Saving All My Love for You'
16. An Emmy Award
17. Whitney
18. 'I Wanna Dance with Somebody (Who Loves Me)'
19. She had seven consecutive No. 1 hits.
20. The Whitney Houston Foundation For Children

Famous Film Quotes – One

1. Tess McGill (Melanie Griffith), Working Girl (1988)
2. Elwood Blues (Dan Aykroyd), The Blues Brothers (1980)
3. Allison Reynolds (Ally Sheedy), The Breakfast Club (1985)
4. Dutch (Arnold Schwarzenegger), Predator (1987)
5. Aurora Greenway (Shirley MacLaine), Terms of Endearment (1983)
6. Mouth (Corey Feldman), The Goonies (1985)
7. Cecilia (Mia Farrow), The Purple Rose of Cairo (1985)
8. Axel Foley (Eddie Murphy), Beverly Hills Cop (1984)
9. Michael 'Crocodile' Dundee (Paul Hogan), Crocodile Dundee (1986)
10. Indiana Jones (Harrison Ford), Raiders of the Lost Ark (1981)
11. Sir (Albert Finney), The Dresser (1983)
12. Jack Torrance (Jack Nicholson), The Shining (1980)
13. Scott Turner (Tom Hanks), Turner & Hooch (1989)
14. Dolores Benedict (Kathleen Turner), The Man with Two Brains (1983)
15. John McClane (Bruce Willis), Die Hard (1988)
16. Prince Vultan (Brian Blessed), Flash Gordon (1980)
17. Harry Callahan (Clint Eastwood), Sudden Impact (1983)
18. John Rambo (Sylvester Stallone), Rambo: First Blood (1982)
19. Alia (Alicia Witt), Dune (1984)
20. The Lord of Darkness (Tim Curry), Legend (1985)

Answers

New Wave Pop

1. Orchestral Manoeuvres in the Dark
2. Adam Ant
3. Bananarama
4. 'True'
5. Soft Cell
6. Duran Duran
7. Talking Heads
8. 'Blue Monday'
9. Billy Idol
10. West End Girls
11. Frankie Goes to Hollywood
12. Stock Aitken Waterman
13. Thompson Twins
14. Gary Numan
15. Boy George
16. Tears for Fears
17. Martin Fry
18. 'Geno' by Dexys Midnight Runners
19. A Flock of Seagulls
20. 'Don't You Want Me'

Eighties Sport – One

1. Nigel Short
2. Jackie Joyner-Kersee
3. John Lowe
4. Ian Rush
5. Italy
6. 800m
7. Manchester United
8. Florence Griffith-Joyner
9. 'Boléro'
10. Carl Lewis
11. Daley Thompson
12. Willie Thorne
13. 1985
14. United States
15. Mary Decker
16. Linford Christie
17. £20,000
18. It was the BBC's first live league game
19. The Boston Celtics
20. Dennis Lillee

Power Ballads

1. 'If I Could Turn Back Time' – Cher
2. 'Total Eclipse of the Heart' – Bonnie Tyler
3. 'China in Your Hand' – T'Pau
4. 'Every Rose Has Its Thorn' – Poison
5. 'All Out of Love' – Air Supply
6. 'Dancing in the Dark' – Bruce Springsteen
7. 'I Want to Know What Love Is' – Foreigner
8. 'Dead Ringer for Love' – Meat Loaf
9. 'Hard to Say I'm Sorry' – Chicago
10. 'Heaven Is a Place On Earth' – Belinda Carlisle
11. 'The Power of Love' – Huey Lewis and the News
12. 'Africa' – Toto
13. 'Is This Love' – Whitesnake
14. 'The Final Countdown' – Europe
15. 'China In Your Hand' – T'Pau
16. 'Livin' on a Prayer' – Bon Jovi
17. 'Don't Stop Believin'' – Journey
18. '(I Just) Died In Your Arms' – Cutting Crew
19. 'Alone' – Heart
20. 'Nothing's Gonna Stop Us Now' – Starship
21. 'Up Where We Belong' – Joe Cocker & Jennifer Warnes
22. 'Broken Wings' – Mr Mister
23. 'Can't Fight This Feeling' – REO Speedwagon
24. 'Listen to Your Heart' – Roxette
25. 'Drive' – The Cars
26. 'We Don't Need Another Hero' – Tina Turner
27. 'Kayleigh' – Marillion
28. 'Holding Out for a Hero' – Bonnie Tyler
29. 'Black Velvet' – Alannah Myles
30. 'Against All Odds (Take A Look At Me Now)' – Phil Collins

Eighties Idols - Madonna

1. The Breakfast Club
2. 'Everybody'
3. 'Burning Up'
4. 'Holiday'
5. Like a Virgin
6. Marilyn Monroe
7. Desperately Seeking Susan
8. A Certain Sacrifice
9. She tried to buy the rights from the director for $5,000. When this failed she tried to get it banned.
10. The Beastie Boys
11. 'Papa Don't Preach'
12. Who's That Girl
13. Sean Penn
14. 'Like a Prayer'
15. Like a Prayer
16. 'Express Yourself'
17. Cameron Alborzian
18. Without the heart there can be no understanding between the hand and the mind.
19. 'Gambler'
20. Material Girl

Back to the Future

1. Eric Stoltz
2. Spaceman From Pluto
3. 1985
4. Jennifer
5. 88 miles per hour
6. Pepsi
7. Her father almost ran over him with his car
8. Billy Zane
9. Einstein
10. 'Johnny B. Goode'
11. 1.21
12. The Flux Capacitor
13. Plutonium
14. 'The Power of Love'
15. Calvin Klein
16. Doc Brown's
17. It was the theme of the high school dance where Marty's parents fell in love
18. 'OUTATIME'
19. Libyan
20. Crispin Glover

Eighties Political Quotes

1. Margaret Thatcher (January 1980)
2. Shirley Williams (July 1980)
3. David Steel (September 1980)
4. Margaret Thatcher (October 1980)
5. Harold Wilson (November 1980)
6. Neil Kinnock (January 1981)
7. Norman Tebbit (October 1981)
8. Margaret Thatcher (June 1982)
9. Gerald Kaufman (March 1983)
10. Ken Livingstone (May 1983)
11. Neil Kinnock (June 1983)
12. Neil Kinnock (October 1983)
13. Tony Benn (March 1984)
14. Ronald Reagan (August 1984)
15. Ken Livingstone (October 1985)
16. Michael Meacher (July 1986)
17. Tam Dalyell (February 1987)
18. Gerald Kaufman (February 1987)
19. Margaret Thatcher (October 1987)
20. Nigel Lawson (October 1989)

Star Wars

1. Luke Starkiller
2. Merchandising rights
3. Yoda
4. C-3PO
5. R2-D2
6. The Millennium Falcon
7. Chewbacca
8. True
9. All of them
10. Never
11. Reel 2 Dialogue Track 2 (editor's shorthand for cans of film on American Graffiti)
12. $10,000
13. Tatooine
14. A hamburger with an olive on the side
15. Zulu
16. Irvin Kershner
17. Chewbacca
18. Alec Guinness
19. Orson Welles
20. Alec Guinness

Sitcoms - One

1. Open All Hours
2. Judi Dench
3. Terry & June
4. Carla Lane
5. The New Statesman
6. Jim Hacker
7. Jimmy Nail
8. Diane Keen
9. 'Allo 'Allo!
10. Desmond's
11. Last of the Summer Wine
12. Bread
13. Birds of a Feather
14. City Lights
15. 1972
16. Maplins
17. Only Fools and Horses
18. Blackadder
19. Kenneth Cranham
20. Filthy Rich & Catflap

Famous Film Quotes - Two

1. Harry Burns (Billy Crystal), When Harry Met Sally (1989)
2. Ferris Bueller (Matthew Broderick), Ferris Bueller's Day Off (1986)
3. Ripley (Sigourney Weaver), Aliens (1986)
4. Dr Rumack (Leslie Nielsen), Airplane! (1980)
5. Roy Batty (Rutger Hauer), Blade Runner (1982)
6. Tony Montana (Al Pacino), Scarface (1983)
7. Dr Peter Venkman (Bill Murray), Ghostbusters (1984)
8. Gordie Lachance (Wil Wheaton), Stand By Me (1986)
9. Joseph Merrick (John Hurt), The Elephant Man (1980)
10. Carol Anne Freeling (Heather O'Rourke), Poltergeist (1982)
11. Mr Miyagi (Pat Morita), The Karate Kid (1984)
12. Maverick (Tom Cruise) and Goose (Anthony Edwards), Top Gun (1986)
13. Dr Emmett Brown (Christopher Lloyd), Back to the Future (1985)
14. Darth Vader (David Prowse/James Earl Jones), The Empire Strikes Back (1980)
15. Bill S. Preston (Alex Winter) and/or Ted 'Theodore' Logan (Keanu Reeves), Bill & Ted's Excellent Adventure (1989)
16. Raymond Babbit (Dustin Hoffman), Rain Man (1988)
17. Veronica Quaife (Geena Davis), The Fly (1986)
18. Johnny Castle (Patrick Swayze), Dirty Dancing (1987)
19. Elise McKenna (Jane Seymour), Somewhere in Time (1980)
20. Zack Mayo (Richard Gere), An Officer and a Gentleman (1982)

E.T. the Extra-Terrestrial

1. 1982
2. Harvey
3. Reese's Pieces
4. Potato Salad
5. 'Be good'
6. He developed a telepathic connection with E.T. who was back home drunk on beer.
7. By copying Gertie as she watched Sesame Street
8. They dressed him as a ghost
9. Cowgirl
10. Chrysanthemum
11. Speak & Spell
12. He held a thermometer next to a lamp to heat it up
13. Real doctors
14. He and E.T. used telepathy to make them fly.
15. Spielberg stated that E.T. is neither male nor female.
16. All of the adults apart from Elliot's mum
17. In mainly chronological order
18. John Williams
19. Jurassic Park
20. Gandhi

Answers

Name the Actress in Both Films

1. Jane Fonda
2. Carrie Fisher
3. Sean Young
4. Daryl Hannah
5. Anjelica Huston
6. Sigourney Weaver
7. Elizabeth McGovern
8. Debra Winger
9. Kelly McGillis
10. Molly Ringwald
11. Sissy Spacek
12. Mia Farrow
13. Anne Bancroft
14. Helen Mirren
15. Cher
16. Glenn Close
17. Michelle Pfeiffer
18. Maggie Smith
19. Jamie Lee Curtis
20. Kathleen Turner
21. Geena Davis
22. Meryl Streep
23. Jessica Lange
24. Whoopi Goldberg
25. Kim Basinger
26. Meg Ryan
27. Nastassja Kinski
28. Rosanna Arquette
29. Helena Bonham Carter
30. Isabella Rossellini

Eighties Fashion

1. The Mullet
2. The Swatch
3. Crimping iron
4. Harrington jacket
5. Scrunchie
6. Alexis Colby (Carrington)
7. Katharine Hamnett
8. Madonna
9. Sade
10. Parachute pants
11. Jane Fonda
12. Hair band
13. Sonny Crockett
14. Nike Air Max 1
15. The red jacket worn by Michael Jackson in his Thriller video
16. Top Gun
17. Vivienne Westwood and Malcolm McLaren
18. Shoulder pads
19. Bananarama
20. Kangol

Eighties Sport – Two

1. Niki Lauda
2. 1982
3. Diego Maradona
4. Michael Jordan
5. Steve Tuttle's ice skate slit his jugular vein
6. Boston
7. England
8. Steve Davis
9. Steffi Graf
10. Ayrton Senna
11. Sugar Ray Leonard
12. Björn Borg
13. Steve Cram
14. Greg Louganis
15. Stephen Redgrave
16. First throw over 100m
17. Barry McGuigan
18. Magic Johnson
19. Robin Cousins
20. Aldaniti

Mix Tape: Opening Lines – Name That Tune – Two

1. 'Love Will Tear Us Apart' (Joy Division)
2. 'Under Pressure' (Queen & David Bowie)
3. 'Don't You (Forget About Me)' (Simple Minds)
4. 'Fools Gold' (The Stone Roses)
5. 'Don't Believe The Hype' (Public Enemy)
6. 'Livin' on a Prayer' (Bon Jovi)
7. 'Ashes to Ashes' (David Bowie)
8. 'Blue Monday' (New Order)
9. 'Walk This Way' (Run-D.M.C. and Aerosmith)
10. 'Buffalo Stance' (Neneh Cherry)
11. 'How Soon Is Now' (The Smiths)
12. 'Love Action (I Believe In Love)' (The Human League)
13. 'The Killing Moon' (Echo & The Bunnymen)
14. 'Everybody Wants to Rule the World' (Tears for Fears)
15. 'When Doves Cry' (Prince)
16. 'I Want to Know What Love Is' (Foreigner)
17. 'Time After Time' (Cyndi Lauper)
18. 'Beat It' (Michael Jackson)
19. 'Down Under' (Men at Work)
20. 'Song to the Siren' (This Mortal Coil)

Answers

Sitcoms - Two

1. Three Up, Two Down
2. You Rang, M'Lord?
3. After Henry
4. Only When I Laugh
5. Home to Roost
6. Never the Twain
7. Bread
8. Watching
9. Fresh Fields
10. Just Good Friends
11. Sorry!
12. Desmond's
13. Keep it in the Family
14. May to December
15. In Sickness and in Health
16. That's My Boy
17. Ever Decreasing Circles
18. Don't Wait Up
19. Up The Elephant And Round The Castle
20. Shelley

Eighties Game Shows

1. 1966
2. Play Your Cards Right
3. Give Us a Clue
4. Wheel of Fortune
5. The Great Egg Race
6. Les Dawson
7. The Krypton Factor
8. Kenneth Kendall
9. 'Chase me!'
10. Mr and Mrs
11. Jim Bowen (on Bullseye)
12. Winner Takes All
13. Henry Kelly
14. False. It was a session musician called Raphael Ravenscroft
15. Leslie Crowther
16. Dusty Bin
17. Countdown
18. Bob Monkhouse
19. Larry Grayson
20. Every Second Counts

Eighties Sport - Three

1. Men's 100m final in the 1988 Olympics
2. Michael Spinks
3. Tessa Sanderson
4. Diego Maradona's 'Hand of God' handball goal that knocked England out of the World Cup quarter-final
5. 1983
6. Mike Gatting
7. Nigel Mansell
8. Ian Botham
9. Aston Villa
10. Daley Thompson
11. Steve Davis
12. Tony Adams
13. Martina Navratilova
14. 1988
15. Carl Lewis
16. Halifax Town
17. Shergar
18. You cannot be serious!
19. Javelin
20. Steve Cram

Eighties Soap Operas

1. Take the High Road
2. General Hospital
3. The Sullivans
4. Young Doctors
5. Sons and Daughters
6. A Country Practice
7. Brookside
8. Neighbours
9. EastEnders
10. Coronation Street
11. Triangle
12. Emmerdale Farm
13. Angels
14. Albion Market
15. The Bill
16. Crossroads
17. Gems
18. Howard's Way
19. Casualty
20. Dallas

Fads and Crazes

1. Pac-Man
2. Deely Boppers
3. Cabbage Patch Doll
4. Sony Walkman
5. BABY ON BOARD
6. Soda Stream
7. History
8. Transformers
9. Scratch n' sniff
10. Donkey Kong
11. Raleigh Grifter
12. Filofax
13. Game & Watch
14. Lycra/Spandex
15. Shrinky Dinks
16. Simon
17. Rubik's Cube
18. Combat
19. Chicken Kiev
20. Scientific calculator watch

Eighties Idols – Prince

1. Prince Rogers Nelson
2. Epilepsy
3. Skipper
4. 'Funk Machine'
5. Dirty Mind
6. Prince
7. Paisley Park Records
8. He was a Jehovah's Witness.
9. The Revolution
10. 5ft 2" (1.57m)
11. He topped the charts with an album (Purple Rain), film (Purple Rain) and single ('When Doves Cry') simultaneously.
12. Purple Rain
13. 'Nothing Compares 2 U'
14. 'When Doves Cry'
15. Like A Prayer
16. Camille
17. 'Lemon Sorbet'
18. 1999
19. The Black Album
20. He changed his name to a 'love symbol' and also became known as 'The Artist Formerly Known as Prince'

Famous TV Catchphrases

1. Buck Rogers in the 25th Century
2. The Kenny Everett Television Show
3. Family Fortunes
4. Red Dwarf
5. Only Fools and Horses
6. Boys from the Blackstuff
7. The Young Ones
8. Cheers
9. 'Allo 'Allo!
10. Danger Mouse/ Charlie Brown
11. Sorry!
12. Blackadder
13. Blockbusters
14. The A-Team
15. The Young Ones
16. Only Fools and Horses
17. Hi-de-Hi!
18. Saved by the Bell
19. Bullseye
20. Dave Allen

The Eighties – Coronation Street

1. Ena Sharples
2. Nick Tilsley
3. Ken and Deidre Barlow
4. Deirdre Barlow
5. Len Fairclough
6. Elsie Tanner
7. Stan Ogden
8. Kevin Webster
9. Mike Baldwin
10. A cat called Rommel
11. A hairdressing salon
12. Mike Baldwin and Susan Barlow
13. A Vauxhall Nova
14. Bet Lynch
15. Brian Tilsley and Ian Latimer
16. Alec Gilroy
17. Hilda Ogden
18. Mavis Riley and Derek Wilton
19. Bet Lynch
20. Alan Bradley

Answers

One Hit Wonders

1. Fern Kinney
2. 'Suicide is Painless'
3. St Winifred's
4. 'Shaddap You Face'
5. Charlene
6. 'Pump Up the Volume'
7. 'First Time'
8. The Electric Light Orchestra
9. David Bowie
10. Chess
11. Aretha Franklin
12. Paul McCartney and Stevie Wonder
13. 'Under Pressure'
14. The Young Ones
15. 'Jack Your Body'
16. The Timelords
17. 'Ferry Cross the Mersey'
18. 'The Chicken Song'
19. 'Love Me Tender'
20. To fly

Eighties Panel Games

1. Robert Robinson
2. I'm Sorry I Haven't a Clue
3. Mastermind
4. Clement Freud
5. Kenneth Williams
6. The News Quiz
7. Arthur Marshall
8. Pop Quiz
9. A Question of Sport
10. Through the Keyhole
11. Catchphrase
12. John Leslie
13. Jeremy Beadle
14. Ask the Family
15. Name That Tune
16. Fred Housego
17. Samantha
18. Fifteen to One
19. Richard Whiteley
20. 'Say what you see.'

The Royal Wedding

1. 1981
2. St Paul's Cathedral
3. 20
4. 32
5. King Juan Carlos I of Spain
6. 3,500
7. Elizabeth and David Emanuel
8. Pearls
9. 7.6 m
10. The Archbishop of Canterbury, Dr Robert Runcie
11. Philip Charles Arthur George
12. He said he would share 'thy goods' instead of 'my worldly goods'
13. No
14. 'Pomp and Circumstance'
15. Lord Lichfield
16. 120
17. 27 Wedding cakes
18. Charles's stag party
19. £30 million
20. 1996

Science Fiction on Television

1. Knight Industries Two Thousand
2. Happy Days
3. Shazbot
4. Max Headroom
5. Twiki
6. Dr Theopolis
7. Wilma
8. Liberator
9. Orac
10. Mining ship
11. Norman Lovett
12. Kryten
13. Peter Davison
14. Richard Griffiths
15. Paul McGann
16. Mark Wing-Davey
17. Sandra Dickinson
18. The Day of the Triffids
19. Sapphire & Steel
20. Star Cops

Live Aid

1. 13th July 1985
2. Bob Geldof and Midge Ure
3. Jack Nicholson
4. The Coldstream Guards band opened with 'God Save the Queen'
5. 'Bohemian Rhapsody'
6. Freddie Mercury
7. Tina Turner
8. The Who
9. Phil Collins
10. Concorde
11. Noel Edmonds
12. Joan Baez
13. 'Bad'
14. Commercial breaks
15. Led Zeppelin
16. Paul McCartney
17. 'All You Need is Love'
18. Ronnie Wood
19. Andy Kershaw
20. Pete Townshend and Paul McCartney

Name the Actor

1. Clint Eastwood
2. Eddie Murphy
3. Sean Connery
4. Richard Gere
5. Michael J. Fox
6. Nicolas Cage
7. Kevin Costner
8. Christopher Walken
9. James Spader
10. Al Pacino
11. Tom Cruise
12. Emilio Estevez
13. Arnold Schwarzenegger
14. Tom Hanks
15. Harrison Ford
16. Mickey Rourke
17. Matthew Broderick
18. Dustin Hoffman
19. Robert De Niro
20. Sylvester Stallone
21. Bruce Willis
22. Steve Guttenberg
23. Michael Douglas
24. John Malkovich
25. Daniel Day-Lewis
26. Willem Dafoe
27. Kiefer Sutherland
28. Jack Nicholson
29. Robin Williams
30. Bill Murray

Alternative Comedy

1. Alexei Sayle
2. Peter Richardson
3. Bad News
4. The Dangerous Brothers
5. Alfresco
6. They were drama teacher students at the Central School of Speech and Drama
7. Nigel Planer
8. SPG (Special Patrol Group)
9. Ben Elton
10. Five Go Mad on Mescalin
11. The landlord in The Young Ones (played by Alexei Sayle)
12. Christopher Ryan
13. Girls on Top
14. Robbie Coltrane
15. Kevin Turvey
16. Jo Brand
17. The Supergrass
18. Raw Sex
19. Keith Allen
20. Stavros

Advertising - Two

1. Heineken
2. Monster Munch
3. Kia-Ora
4. Milk
5. Lilt
6. Jacobs Club
7. Trio
8. Timotei
9. Oxo
10. Glow
11. Twix
12. Ferrero Rocher
13. Kellogg's Start
14. Skol
15. Crunchie
16. Golden Churn
17. Hellmann's Mayonnaise
18. Hermesetas Sweetener
19. HP Sauce
20. Kellogg's Special K

The King of Pop: Michael Jackson

1. Gary, Indiana, USA
2. Joseph
3. He sustained burns when an explosion set his hair on fire
4. Thriller
5. The publishing rights to the Beatles back catalogue
6. Exeter City
7. 8
8. Lionel Richie
9. Pinocchio
10. To remind people of the suffering of children around the world
11. Twice
12. 'I Can't Go for That (No Can Do)'
13. Martin Scorsese
14. It was the first video by a black artist to air on MTV
15. Moonwalk
16. Fred Astaire
17. Bubbles
18. Boa constrictor
19. $17 million
20. Vitiligo

Characters in the Eighties – EastEnders

1. Ali Osman
2. Donna Ludlow
3. Barry Clark
4. Lou Beale
5. Angie Watts
6. Lofty Holloway
7. Elizabeth Beale
8. Duncan Boyd
9. Den Watts
10. Arthur Fowler
11. Ethel Skinner
12. Willy the pug
13. Pauline Fowler
14. Reg Cox
15. Nick Cotton
16. Sue Osman
17. Roly Watts
18. Michelle Fowler
19. Dot Cotton
20. Simon Wicks ('Wicksy')

Blackadder

1. 1983
2. Edmund
3. Brian Blessed
4. Alnwick Castle
5. Rowan Atkinson and Richard Curtis
6. Ben Elton
7. 'I have a cunning plan.'
8. Jennifer Saunders
9. Baldrick
10. Hugh Laurie
11. Melchett
12. Mrs Miggins
13. Miranda Richardson
14. Rik Mayall
15. She is a woman and she is wise.
16. Baldrick
17. Dad's Army
18. Flashheart
19. So he would be declared mad and get sent home
20. Baldrick